Coolie Location

Jay Naidoo

SA Writers

London

SA Writers
25a Greencroft Gardens, London NW6 3LN

Taurus,
PO Box 39400, Bramley 2018, Johannesburg

First published 1990 in Great Britain by SA Writers
and in southern Africa by Taurus

ISBN 1 872086 03 9

Set in 10/12 Trump Medieval by Robert Vicat Ltd, London
Printed and bound in Great Britain by
by Cox and Wyman, Reading, Berkshire

For all the people of the Pretoria Location

Acknowledgement

I am grateful to Pierette Nadeau, Jacques Carlucci, Agnes Bairn, Joan Finlay, Jack and Stella Hyams and Marie-Annick Lhuilier for having read and commented on different drafts of this book.

A version of Chapter five was published as "Sunday Football" in *Contrast*, 17, 2 (1988) and Chapter Twenty as "Old Block" in the *Southern African Review of Books*, 3, 3 & 4 (February/May 1990).

1

Nothing is as inevitable as birth and death. We all come and we all go. I came in the year when Operation Barbarossa was launched. I'm always astonished by those who can tell you pat what day and what hour of the day they came into the world. I cannot. But I do know I was born at home. I had three brothers and a sister waiting for me and, three years later, I did the waiting for a sister. My two elder brothers, Bobby and Sonny, were almost grown men and belonged to another generation. Ranga, a few years older than myself was, in many ways, the only brother I had.

Jerusalem Street, where I was born, was part of the Asiatic Bazaar and the Asiatic bazaar was part of the Location. Of course, officially the Location didn't exist, but it was there all right, a mile from the city of Pretoria, a mile from the capital, a mile from the heart of white South Africa.

Von Wielligh Street in the west, Struben Street in the south, the *Kaakdraai*, where the city's sewerage was treated, in the north, and a bridge, a wire fence, another bridge, a bus depot and a stream in the east severed it and separated it from white Pretoria. Dusty streets, as if the Location was a grid iron, divided it into blocks. Boom Street, the main street, was a white street. It slipped in from one white end and scuttled away towards another. It was tarred, and so were Cowie and Jerusalem because they carried through traffic — Blood, Grand and Barber were tarred as well but only the white officials who ran the municipality knew why.

The Location's morning winter air seared the fingers until the sun, at about ten o'clock in the morning, banished the misty chill. Winter evenings, however, were harsh and huddlingly cold. It was on one such evening, quiet and typical,

1

that my life, as it lives on in my memory, comes alive. We were all, apart from my parents, in the kitchen — my father was still at the market and my mother was somewhere about the house. Ruby and Ambi, my sisters, and I were seated close together in front of the warm coal stove. Ranga, my brother, seated at a table was busy with his homework.

The heat made everyone, including Jessie, the family cat (snugly asleep upon my lap), feel warm and safe. I watched the red-hot coal trapped behind the black iron grid. The forming and crumbling embers, and the crackling and hissing flames enchanted me. I could feel the steady warmth, could feel the heat wrapping itself around my bare legs and crawling up my skinny belly. No foetus could have been more comfortable.

Ambi, my younger sister, was already dozing when suddenly I felt something strange move between my legs. A marble-white object, thin and smooth, slid off my thigh, slipped over the edge of the bench and landed in a whisper on the floorboard. Taken aback, as only an infant can be taken aback, I instinctively connected what I had felt and seen with the mystery of the red embers and let slip the cry of "Fire! Fire! Fire!" Ambi, startled from her sleep, burst out crying. My mother, alarmed, rushed into the kitchen.

I see her now with her *mookootee,* her sad long-suffering face, her uncanny ability to read my mind, her ready smile and her delicious fat arms that quivered like jelly when she laughed. And I smell her: coconut oil, turmeric, Madras cotton, Lifebouy soap and Five Roses tea.

My uncontrolled shouts of fire made my mother turn pale. I was already on my feet when she grabbed me by the hand and, in one swift movement, tore me out of the kitchen. My shouts of "fire!" went on. She examined me, sharp and brusque, but found nothing. Then, after a brief moment of hesitation, she confiscated my trousers.

My own reaction surprised me; like a cat stricken with fear, I abandoned myself to her control. She inspected me again, hesitated a little and then, without warning, let fly with a series of slaps, which fell short and sharp on my unprotected thighs and calves. It was the only time that she

2

had laid hands on me. The burning pain and the reluctant tears silenced my cry.

The punishment might have continued, if my brother had not come out of the kitchen holding a long thin piece of fire-wood in his hand.

"Hamma!" he called, as he displayed the stick with a self-satisfaction as evident as his bemusement.

"Did that come from him, Ranga?" she asked, her voice betraying bewilderment.

Yes, he nodded.

I watched this exchange in rapt silence. I wondered about the mystery of my involuntary conduct. My mother unexpectedly turned all gentle. She put her hand on my head, ruffled my hair and, in a cuddling, endearing movement, pressed me against her thigh. I felt the soft warm texture of her familiar cotton sari on my cheeks. I looked up at her and, though my eyes were misty, my legs sore and brain muddled, I felt comforted and safe again. Hamma, I asked with my eyes, what was this strange thing that happened to me?

"Oh, it's just a tapeworm, Jay. Tomorrow, you must have some castor oil, in case you've got another one that wants to come out."

* * *

I was lying in bed with my eyes wide open. There was a crack in the curtain and a dim light crossed the ceiling like a faded chalk marking on a football ground. My sisters, on the bed at the opposite end of the long room, were fast asleep. My ears picked up a faint but unmistakable sound of dispute and quarrel.

"It's the Hopolong Cassidy cajee they're showing at the Royal."

I twisted around, pulled the sheet over my head and tried to shut out the noise, but my ears were recalcitrant. I reached for the curtain but before widening the crack, I checked to see if Ruby and Ambi were still asleep. Ruby was always ready to play the big sister. I could just hear her saying: "Jay, what are you doing? Close that curtain! I'll tell Hamma!" But

3

she and Ambi had closed down for the day. I stretched myself out on to my knees. The street lights and the yellow neon lights from Lalie's Café, displaying FISH & CHI S, were still on. I pressed my forehead against the cool glass pane and peered into the shadowy light: I saw three men.

"No. No man, you can't go just like that!"

"Hey brother, don't be like that. I must go now. It's late man."

"Look at this guy. He takes the cake. He's been doing all the winning and now he wants to vamoose, just like that — 'Ah, hard luck ou, you've lost, now I'm vacating'. That's too bloody easy, man."

"Hey brother, take it easy man. Tomorrow is another day. You know you can't always win."

"Hey, watch it ou! You mean I can't stick a lose nè? That's what you're saying. You hear that? This guy is telling me that I can't take a lose. Hey, who're you thinking you're talking to? This is Bra Brakes, who plays for stakes and who never fakes — Bra Brakes man!"

And with that Bra Brakes struck his fist into his antagonist's face. Pandemonium broke out.

I heard a sharp crack. I froze. My heart pounded away like bass drums. Bra Brakes's victim picked up a huge stone. There was a scuffle. Something flashed. Someone fell. Shadows, like swooping bats, darted away. Silence.

My body came out in a quake. I fell back into bed and covered my head. Later, much later, I opened my eyes. The light-line across the ceiling was gone. I noticed that my pyjamas around my chest and back were wet. I turned my head towards the left and scanned the curtain. The crack was still visible but no light filtered through. I got on to my knees again and, regardless of my sisters, peered through the window. No street lights. Everything outside was black and silent.

I slid back into bed, got up again and scrutinized the obscurity but couldn't see a thing. A nightmare? There were times when I couldn't distinguish between dream and reality. When during the night I wanted to relieve myself, I would go to the toilet and while urinating with pleasure and pride discover that I was busy wetting my bed.

4

Should I go and wake up Ruby? No, she'd only squeal or, worse still, laugh at me. Best go to sleep. I felt drained and drowsy. Sleep came quick and fast.

The following morning , after washing my face in the outdoor bathroom, I entered the kitchen to have my usual breakfast of coffee, toast and butter. My mother was there busy stirring some coffee in an old enamel mug.

"Did the police come?"

"Yes Auntie. Vroeg this morning!"

I pricked up my ears and signalled, with my eyes, a greeting to both my mother and Lena.

Lena, my Aunt Kootie's African "girl", spoke Tamil, when she wanted to, better even than I did. She had been so long with Auntie Kootie that everybody considered her part of my aunt's family. It had become a habit of hers to cross the street in the mornings and to pay a ritual social call to my mother. There were always bits of local family news to be exchanged or messages to be delivered; and there was always a mug of coffee and some thick-sliced bread waiting to welcome her.

"I told Kootie that one day somebody's going to get killed there. Ag Heere Auntie! Gambling is no good. Dice and fight gaan altyd saam. You know that man they stabbed, ag, he was so mekaar that he wanted to walk home. But Auntie he didn't go far nè. He fell just in front of our place. The police came. Hulle het hom weg geneem. It was a good thing the children were still sleeping. Auntie, there was so much blood — it was all over the place. I said, 'Lena you can't leave it like that'. I took a besem and covered the blood with sand."

I gulped down the rest of my breakfast, slipped out of the kitchen, met Ambi in the yard, grabbed her by the hand and commandeered her: "Come with me! I'm going to show you something!"

The heavy blobs on the sand pavement, though hastily covered, were still visible. My sister and I, like Hansel and Gretel, followed the signs. A large silent stain on the stoep of Lalie's Café brought us to an abrupt halt. "Hey, look Jay!" Ambi tittered, and pointing to the floor, said, "It looks like your shadow."

2

Uncle Ganes invited me into his room. It was less than half an hour before we set out with the rest of the Location for the traditional picnic at Hennop River on the one day when the Location quit its confines and ventured into foreign white territory.

Uncle Ganes had a gruff but jovial voice. His premature grey hair, moustache and squat figure accentuated that benignity that I always assumed was the natural endowment of a mature adult.

"Are you thirsty boy?"

Yes, I nodded.

He gave me a small glass of water filled to the brim. I was thirsty; I gulped down the drink. He observed me with twinkling eyes. I felt sure that he was going to put his hand into his pocket and pull out a tickey. Instead he patted me on the back and said, "Atta boy!" I gave him my usual smile of obedience.

Ten minutes later, I was on the back of the open Dodge truck with my brothers, sisters and an assemblage of cousins. A corner of the vehicle was reserved for the indispensable picnic wherewithal: pots, which individually contained rice and an assortment of curries; three large watermelons; boxes of mangoes, lichees and peaches; and boxes of Coca Cola, Hubbly Bubbly and Tingaling.

Ambi, pointing to a box, asked me: "Are they peach or kidney mangoes?"

"Peach."

"Oh good, I hate the kidney ones. The hairs get into your teeth and you can never get them out."

Ranga, Ruby and my cousins, Boya and Praga, were all

excited and jumping about. The sight of the mangoes and the thought of food turned my stomach. My legs wobbled. I sought and found a vacant spot against one of the sides, and my drained body occupied the space like a bag of discarded potatoes.

The truck set off, the Location fell behind and we were soon on the open road. Sitting up was, I found, impossible. My body fell back and my legs splayed forward. Above, the dark heavy boughs of the plane trees raced by on a blue veld turned upside down. My head spun and my stomach heaved. Light and shade blinked and ran across my stomach. My hands and scalp moistened and, before I could grasp what was happening, I turned, jerked forward and spewed. The retching, just missing Ruby, splattered the metal side of the truck with a mangoeish hue. Although Ruby was both startled and puzzled, she held my head so that I could vomit without polluting the vehicle. The road was deserted. The mess fell and streaked along the tarmac like a drunken no-parking line; my head spun and I vomited again. After bringing up a third and fourth time, the dizziness eased off and my stomach settled down but I felt too weak to do anything but breathe.

When we reached the picnic spot, Ruby dutifully reported my malaise to my father.

"How come you were sick?"

"Don't know."

He looked anxious. It was strange when he showed concern in this way. I could swear he was entirely different from the man who, with a mere frown, could strike fear into my little heart.

"What did you eat this morning?"

"Coffee and butter bread."

"Didn't you have anything else before you got on to the truck? Didn't you eat too many lichees?"

He knew I was a glutton for lichees but I assured him: "No — I didn't eat any fruit. I didn't eat anything — I only had a glass of water."

"Water?"

"Yes. Uncle Ganes gave me a glass of water just before we

left." He greeted my words with disbelief. I hurriedly added: "You can ask him yourself!"

Turning away from father's look of shock and bewilderment, and reaching out for assurance, I searched out for my uncle. We found him clutching a near-empty bottle and happily slumped down against a twisted thorn tree. A rough blanket (incongruously unoccupied) lay stretched out beside him and, next to the blanket, an outstretched hand and a familiar glass, which lay desolately tipped over and spent.

* * *

I see Johannesburg Papa's face now — Jopa, my mother's father — a handsome amazon face. I never could picture this herbalist grandfather of mine among the weird roots, strange seeds and the bizarre assortment of skins, tails and horns. There was one thing about him: he could, unlike my parents, read and write — he was, as the Location would say, clever.

One day a white door-to-door salesman came to the house. The one thing that our house, 226 Jerusalem Street, did not have was books and now this white man took out two enormous maroon volumes: *The New Century Dictionary*. He wanted five guineas for them. Jopa seemed interested. He took the books from the white man and laid them out carefully on the glass top of the walnut dining-room table. I was dutifully seated at the table, practically under his nose. When the volume was opened, a sweet dark scent of virgin binding and crisp paper rose and intoxicated my senses with the romance of learning. The small print on the pages was illustrated with little drawings. My grandfather carefully turned and scanned the pages. When he came to page 2047, he paused, closed the volume and said, "All right, I'll take it."

When the man had gone, I asked Jopa: "How is it you decided to buy so quickly?"

"I saw that it was a very good dictionary."

"But ..."

"An English dictionary which has this, is a good dictionary."

8

My grandfather opened the second volume again and read slow and deliberately: "Trimurthi: the Hindu triad or trinity, Brahma, Vishnu and Siva (regarded respectively as the creative, the preserving, and the destroying principle), viewed as an inseparable unity, and represented symbolically as one body with three heads."

The names Brahma, Vishnu and Siva were familiar to my ears but I couldn't understand what Trimurthi was — except that he had three heads; for I had looked at the picture while my grandfather was reading. The old man, I sensed, was waiting for me to ask another question; so I obliged: "Jopa, we are Hindus?"

"Yes."

"What are white people, then?"

"They're Christians."

"Are we Hindus better than Christians?"

The old man laughed: "You mean is Hinduism better than Christianity?"

"Well, is their thing or our thing better?"

"Oh, there aren't better or worse religions, you know. All rivers flow to the sea."

"All rivers flow to the sea? What does that mean?"

"All religions honour God."

"What's God?"

"If you carry on like this, you'll have to call me Dictionary Papa."

I laughed. "Yes, but, Jopa, I can't read."

"All right, somebody has to explain these things to you and it might as well be me. Well, God is the person that made the world, the stars, the moon, your mother, your father, you and me — everybody. God is responsible for everything. He's our master — our boss, our baas."

I looked blankly at my grandfather and then, as if inspired, I came back: "Jopa, how does God look?"

"He looks like Ganes." I frowned and saw my uncle slumped against the thorn tree.

"You know, Ganes, the elephant!"

"Like an elephant?"

"Yes, or like Hanuman."

9

"Hanuman?"

"Yes, you know, the monkey God. Haven't you seen the calendar at your Auntie Kootie's place?"

"Yes!"

"Well, that's Hanuman."

"So God gets up to mischief then?" I saw Hanuman with his tail alight setting fire to an entire city.

My grandfather smiled and airily added: "God isn't always good, you know. You see, our Hindu Gods are like people. That's why we have Trimurthi: a maker, a keeper and a breaker — have you seen a picture of the God Khrishna, you know, where he is painted all blue?"

I nodded hesitantly, as I thought of the calendar I had seen at Abdul Supplies Store.

"Well, some people say that's because he was smoking ganja."

"Smoking ganja! A God that smokes ganja?" I knew enough to realize that *ganja* was only smoked by lay-abouts and ne'er-do-wells. I felt certain that my grandfather was having me on. I turned around in a huff and went searching for my mother. I found her in the kitchen rolling the familiar grey-black grinding stone over a cupful of freshly peeled peanuts.

"Hamma, is it true that God Khrishna smokes ganja?"

"What?"

"Is it true that Sami Khrishna smokes ganja?"

"Oh, get away with your mad nonsense! And stop asking rude questions like that; otherwise I'll have to wash your mouth out with soap!"

* * *

I see my father (because I didn't want to eat) mashing potatoes with rice and butter, and getting me to dig into the mixture with relish; I see my mother cleaning the claws from the crab curry for me; I see my red windup cadillac car which could never fall off the edge of the table; and I see my Auntie Neela, the intellectual of the family, playfully warning me: "Don't say that in front of your father otherwise he'll wash your mouth out with soap!"

How many times did I hear that warning.

I had got into the habit of repeating some of the sayings that adults always seem to use. I found it a delight to say "a friend in need is a friend indeed". Besides, I more or less understood what it meant. When I heard adults saying things like: "And you know Tanga is so good, she helped that poor Doorsammy so much and with never a complaint," I would butt in with: "A friend in need is a friend indeed". Whereupon the adults, surprised, would break out in slightly embarrassed laughter. On one such occasion, Auntie Neela said: "Oh, this one has a fine, cheeky tongue."

Similarly, before I even started going to school, I understood, in general, what "when the cat's away the mice will play" meant. But "an apple a day keeps the doctor away" flummoxed me. I never quite grasped that an apple a day actually meant eating an apple a day. I had this vague idea that if you carried an apple in your pocket all the time the doctor would be kept away. This, I can tell you, got me into trouble with my mother. But it was my liking for the part-English and part-Afrikaans saying which made Auntie Neela issue her "wash your mouth out with soap" warning one Sunday morning.

On Sundays, "Coloured" girls and "Coloured" women, decked out in their finery, passed our house on their way to church service. On their way back, when they turned Grand Street and passed Lalie's Café, it was possible, from the stoep of the house, to see them in all their detail and splendour. It was on such a Sunday (when the cooking had been done, my mother and some aunties were enjoying the sun, and conversing and eyeing the Sunday parade) that beautiful Vera, who, in every way, looked like a European (a little like Debbie Reynolds, but only handsomer and sexier), turned Grand Street and came up past the Café. Even at that tender age, I secretly admired her fine looks and her comely figure — perhaps Vera was my first love. But I knew, from overhearing the women, that her beauty had involved her, sometimes adversely, with several prominent men of the Location — "Coloured", Chinese and Indian.

She approached the house, moving delicately and gracefully

11

on a pair of two-toned pink and charcoal-grey shoes. She had on a homespun pink dress, discreetly decorated with charcoal-grey ribbons and she sported a dainty pink hat. She was in her prime and required no make up to heighten her radiance. When she was about twenty-five yards from the house, the women's voices fell. They cast furtive, envious glances at her. The front door, as usual, was open and from within came the voice of Bing Crosby singing, 'Oh, What a Beautiful Morning'. It was then I said, thinking it was appropriate and strictly complimentary: "New look met 'n ou koek!" The women broke out, without Vera being aware of it, into a spontaneous laugh and they all displayed, including my mother, a superficial expression of shock and a real expression of lascivious gaiety. It was long seconds later that my Auntie Neela warned me not to use the expression in front of my father. Adults, I thought, were sometimes quite bewildering.

3

I noticed quite early in life that Fridays were exceptional:
Ranga and Ruby came home early from school, my mother
— and aunties — had baths and covered their bodies and
faces with *manjatool*, the *vulca* was cleaned and lit and,
most notable of all, the food prepared that day was severely
uniform. Friday was *maracurry* day, the one day in the week
when meat was neither cooked nor eaten at 226. One Friday
(just before lunch) I asked Jopa why Friday was *maracurry*
day.

Grandfather paused. I could see it was the first time that
he had been asked such a question.

"Well, we Hindus are vegetarians. We believe it is wrong
to kill in order to eat."

"But we aren't vegetarians!"

"Yes, of course, but in honour of the fact that we never
used to eat meat, we now make Fridays a no-meat day."

"We never used to eat meat? Was it you, then, who started
eating meat first?"

"No."

"Was it your father, then?"

"No."

"Who then?"

"Well, it was my grandfather — my Jopa!" He chuckled. I
looked at him and tried to picture him as a little boy in short
trousers but I kept seeing him as a *muti* salesman. "Yes, as
far as we Naidoos are concerned, it was my Jopa who started
the meat-eating business."

"Was he naughty?"

"Well, maybe — in a way — he was. But you know, it's
thanks to him that we're here today ... Ah, I can see you're

13

wondering what I'm on about. You see, my grandfather used to live in India — in Andhra Pradesh Province — and one day, when he was still a very young man, he left India."

"Yes, but why did he leave India?"

"God alone knows, Jay. Why does anyone want to leave home? I suppose he was a little mad. You've got to be a little mad to leave home like that. Anyway, he left India and went to Mauritius. There he worked for a French veterinary — a veterinary is an animal doctor — and while working for this doctor he learnt to eat meat. Then he went back to India — as a meat-eater, of course — but his family wouldn't allow him to eat with them; so he decided to come to Natal. And that's how my father was born in Pinetown, in 1880."

"Jopa, do you eat meat on Fridays?"

"No, but if you want to eat meat on Fridays you mustn't let maracurry day stop you."

"Why?"

"Well, meat-eaters are stronger than vegetable-eaters. Just look at the Muslim cricketers; they hit the ball much harder than the Hindu cricketers. And look at the Europeans — real meat-eaters — they hit the ball even harder than the Muslims."

Meat eating was always an act of rebellion in our family. There was this ancestor in Mauritius and my brothers and I with our pork- and beef-eating sessions: vienna and pork sausages, boerewors and Ralph & Clary's hamburgers. My father allowed the illicit foods into the house, but barred them from the kitchen. Come to think of it, meat eating was a potential act of rebellion among all Indians; the Hindus when they consumed beef and pork, and the Muslims when they consumed pork and non-halal beef, mutton and chicken. It was impossible to free oneself from the past, impossible to get away from India.

Late in the winter of 1947, when I was already six, the house and the Location livened up. An atmosphere of wide expectation and deep promise gripped the air — it was the year when India became independent. Jopa and my mother sat glued to the radio, listening to the news and, in the evenings, to the broadcasts coming from New Delhi. Gandhi, Nehru and Jinnah became household names, and so

14

did the name of a new country, Paki
— *Pakistan Zindabad*.

An Indian brigade was formed and
retaliation, a Muslim one was formed
Gandhi cap and in a uniform of w
trousers, I participated in the bold, con
and enthusiastically sang 'Bande Mata
was short-lived: partition brought o
communal violence, Gandhi (a year l
and Jopa was carried off by a stroke.

For the first time, I sensed the division between Hindus
and Muslims, but the thing made no sense to me — not
then, not now. And yet, if anything, division was a hallmark
of South Africa — division in and out, division up and down
and division upside down, inside out and right side up.
Division between white and black, division between Indians
and "Coloureds", and division between Indians and Africans.
When I was almost eight years old, riots in Durban (involv-
ing Indians and Zulus) led to large-scale death and destruc-
tion. After that I recall my mother saying that, though she
had a Transvaal-born father and a Natal-born grandfather, we
were Indians and that India was our motherland. I never
quite followed her in her reasoning; for was I not born in
South Africa and therefore African? Which brings me to
Blackie who, after Lena, was the second African in my life.

Everything about Blackie tended to the extreme: his skin
was black, his teeth were white, his frame was large, his
height was tall, his voice was bass and his laugh was loud.
My father couldn't stand him; my mother, though she suspected he was a rogue, found him amusing and kept him on
almost as a house jester. I loved him — a character, in my
esteem, second only to my grandfather. Years later when
Blackie had fallen out of favour with the family because of
costly and brazen thefts, he would stop and indulgently talk
to me. And while talking to me would be oblivious of the
fact that he was at the time uncomfortably wearing a but-
ton-down Arrow shirt and a Levis blue jeans that had
belonged to me and which, when they disappeared from the
washing line, were almost brand-new.

stens youstens seestens Samsonstens andstens Delila-
ns?" This was how Blackie sometimes spoke, and how he,
one morning, asked me: "Did you see *Samson and Delila*?"

"No," I replied.

"Ag, you must see the way Victor Mature kills a lion with
his bare hands. What a film!" he said in non-Blackie English.

He continued to dust the walnut armchair. I could see that
he had already cleaned the showcase radio-record player.
The Pilot radio was switched on but silent.

"What are you listening to Blackie?" I knew that he liked
cleaning the sitting room because of the radio.

"No, I've just switched it on. Waiting for it to warm up."
He pulled the brass handle on the bottom left side of the
showcase. It fell open and the Garrard record player slid out
like a drawer in a filing cabinet. He then carefully placed his
favourite seventy-eight, Al Debbo's 'Hassie Hoekom is Jou
Stert so Kort?' which he had obtained from Kalla's Cycle
Store — he had in that inimitable way of his persuaded my
mother to let him go and buy it for her. Once the record was
on, he sang and dusted.

I went out on to the stoep. It was a bright clear spring day.
I liked the El Debbo song but I'd heard it so often that it now
wearied me. I chose a wicker chair to sit on and decided I'd
watch the world of Jerusalem Street go by, but the Street was
taking a nap. I felt restless. What to do? I couldn't decide. On
the side of the porch, I saw the banana tree that had always
been a part of the front garden, noticed its new and shiny
foliage, and wondered why the all-vegetable Tamil wedding
meals were always served on these huge leaves.

I grew more restless. I left the stoep. The red cement porch
had just been polished and shined. I trod carefully. I had
already slipped on it once before and had bumped the back of
my head on its merciless surface. The resulting injury produced an egg-like swelling, and, for weeks afterwards caused
Ruby and Ranga to tease me: first by naming and then by
constantly calling me, Knoppie. Outside on the pavement I

might, I hoped, find Boya or someone to play with; but even the pavements were deserted. I turned to go back into the house when, without meaning to, I spotted, in the southern horizon, the tower of the Voortrekker Monument. Suddenly an idea flashed through my mind: I could get the binoculars and go up on to the roof and see how the Monument was coming along.

Two days before Blackie had come to the house with an almost new, massive pair of binoculars. A friend of his, so he told my mother, wanted to sell it for £2. He claimed, with truth, that in town it was worth £15. Mother laughed and said, "What do I want with a pair of binoculars?"

"Yes, but Ranga and Ruby can use it. They can watch the stars, the birds and the trees. Ranga told me the other day that at school he was studying the different birdstens and treestens, and also the moonstens."

She couldn't resist his sale talk but lamented that she was sure she wasn't doing the right thing. That evening when my father returned from the Market, she showed him her purchase. The binoculars impressed him but the transaction did not: "If they steal from others to sell to us, they can steal from us to sell to others!" Mother knew he was right but there was nothing for it; the deed was done. She renounced her act by discarding the back-door article on her dressing-table.

I entered my parents' bedroom, took the binoculars — I was surprised by their weight — raced into the yard, negotiated the narrow space between the rear walls of the bathroom and the toilet, and the pile of empty wooden boxes and crates, and then scaled the two-yard high brick wall that separated 226 from 225. In less than a minute I was on the roof. With the binoculars I was able to see that the construction of the Monument was almost completed. To me it looked like a rectangular vase with a square base turned upside down — grandfather, when he had seen an artist's impression of it, had said it looked like an old-style radio. I found it imposing, harsh and, in some ways, off-putting but the wall encircling the edifice of the tower with its motifs and its embossed ox wagons made me (in contrast) want to approach it and

17

inspect it. Yet nobody in the Location ever thought of visiting the place: it was too remote, too exclusive, too Afrikaner, too white.

I moved the binoculars to the right, peered past the giant eucalyptus tree (just opposite 226), focussed on the hill in the distance and saw the Union Building shrouded in a mauvish haze. It looked serene and supreme and altogether in harmony with its surroundings.

"Hey Jay!"

I turned around and saw Laksmi. She was seated on the ledge of the brick wall that separated our place from that of the Tebba's — the neighbours at the back of 226. She and her family lived behind 225. Their grocery shop and house stood on the corner of Blood and Fourth Streets. She beckoned me with a wave of the hand. I set the binoculars down and got off the roof, rapidly negotiated the ledge and soon reached her — I had done this before and I was protected by construction walls on each side. She invited me to sit next to her. She was a little older than my brother and wasn't particularly good-looking, but her plainness was offset by a fine smooth complexion and by long wavy hair.

"Do you want a sweet?"

Yes, I nodded.

She lifted her plain navy-blue skirt — she had nothing on — and pointed to her uncontrolled black and thick pubic hairs: "Come and touch me here!" I did. She then gave me a sweet, which she took out of her skirt pocket. She smiled and I felt as if I was being patted on the head.

Later I made my way to the nearby gate that provided access to the yard. Blackie, leaning against the fence, was watering the small richly-flowered garden in front of 226. He saw me and, as was his playful wont, deliberately raised the black hose-pipe he was holding and gave me a brief but brisk shower. Without premeditation, the fateful words — the careless words — "Kaffirs have bird brains" came tumbling out of my mouth.

The utterance stung Blackie to the quick. His expansive, Jack Johnson smile was wiped away. I could see he was hurt. Over the sounds of spraying water and heavy dripping,

18

which the lush foliage provided by their deflection, his voice betraying disappointment and an unfamiliar gravity, reproached, "Why do you say that? Don't you know that these are bad words — no-good words used by big people. You shouldn't use words like that. It's not nice to say that. You're too small to say things like that."

I had heard these words before. I had witnessed the hurt my own father's use of them had caused; and I had always, privately, reproached him for using them. Now I had used them myself. I had known instinctively that I had done something wrong the moment the words had escaped my mouth. Now, confused, I felt that I had been had: "Sticks and stones may break my bones but words will never hurt me" was simply not true. Ashamed, I looked at him for a few seconds, murmured, "Sorry," and then swiftly entered the yard.

After I had dried myself hurriedly with the kitchen towel, I settled in a corner brooding and wondering why these words were so important. But, no matter how I tried, I found no satisfactory answer. I kept coming up with pictures and bumping up against stories which only confirmed the opinions adults held of Blackie and other Africans. It was so easy to recall the frequent complaints my mother made about the various "kitchen boys". It was no good, I wasn't able to make sense of it. With Jopa no longer about there was nobody I could ask.

4

"You're a big boy now Jay, tomorrow, lucky fellow, you can go to school with Ruby." My mother uttered these words on a fateful January day, the day before Ranga and Ruby returned to school. The words struck me with terror; I felt I was going to be sick. Tears fell, as if my eyes had suffered a haemorrhage.

The next morning my mother insisted, although I could see she was in sympathy with my plight, that everybody, when they reached the age of six, had to go to school. She and Ruby then set about making me presentable. I had to put on my best short trousers, shirt, socks and shoes. My hair was doused with coconut oil and slicked into shape with the big brown comb that my mother used for her own hair. Ruby insisted on putting some Ponds cream on my face. She applied the sticky stuff on to my cheeks and then, fixing me with her eyes, she said, "You must look nice for the white teacher you're going to have!"

I did not protest at the grooming. I disciplined my limbs into a stubborn tautness and my tongue into a morose silence. I became an automaton and looked as if I had lost all my marbles.

Later I refused to touch the buttered brown slices of toast that I was supposed to have for breakfast. I did have a sip of coffee and milk from my sister's cup because she insisted and also because I didn't know how to say no. Then the three of us, sister, mother and I, left 226 through the yard exit and walked up to the corner of Blood and Jerusalem Streets. There, five blocks to the west, was Lorenz Street and the Pretoria Boys' Indian School. In the distance I saw the faint, shimmering outlines of the School's wire and metal entry gate. On the pavement of Blood Street crushed peanut shells, flattened *pannikies*, the torn or shredded wrappers of various sweets and chewing gums, and bits of glass in all shapes and in all colours, like shells and debris strewn on a beach, littered the sandy ground.

We crossed the corner of Fourth Street and there, after having taken a few steps farther, I was suddenly taken over by a raw panic. I looked at my mother, clutched her orange sari and implored her: "Hamma, I wanna to stay with you! Don't send me to school!" At that very moment a woman, who was busy sweeping the dusty surface in front of her house, looked up, greeted my mother and, without the least bother, incited her not to give in to my supplication.

I did not know the woman but her intrusion — big people, in their stubborn and pig-headed adherence to custom and convention, can sometimes be so cruel — set fire to my guts. I wanted to lash out at her: keep your nose out of our business or something to that effect; I knew that if I ventured to do something so discourteous and rash I would lose all sympathy and my mother, for the sake of correction, would insist that I go to school forthwith. I did instead what my age counselled me to do: I cried.

The flood of tears, the pleading and my sister's fear of being late made my mother reverse her decision to send me to school. I wasn't aware of it at the time but that concession was the contract of a great friendship.

* * *

A year later I went to school not with enthusiasm but without protest. There, I was stunned by the newness of the complicated surroundings. I discovered an exciting new world: the immaculate lawn, the scent of freshly cut grass, the spotlessly clean grounds, the varied colours, shapes and models of the teachers' cars; the red-brick buildings, the Dettol smell of the toilets, the light and shade on the ground made by the young and old poplar trees, the mulberry trees behind the prefab, the woodwork classroom, the hundreds of new faces and — the spruce, mighty and majestic presence of the white teachers.

21

My first teacher was Mrs Wymann, a wrinkled woman, who wore a dark hairnet to keep her sparse brown locks in place. The net heightened her formidable look. Her favourite apparel seemed to be a dark brown gaberdine dress worn over an evident corset. She changed outfits regularly but somehow she always seemed to be dressed in the same brown dress. Her thin lips, which must have been already slight in her youth, now disappeared into her small nervous mouth. Her hands with prominent veins were large and powerful.

Mrs Armoury who taught a higher grade was Mrs Wymann's bosom friend. They were always visiting each other, during playtime, before classes and after classes. They never called each other by name; it was always a gentle, Koo-wie; so it was inevitable that they were nicknamed Koo-wie One and Koo-wie Two.

Mrs Wymann's frequent visits to her friend meant that the classroom was often left unattended. One day, after such a visit, she returned infuriated because the class had had the temerity to talk and to be excited during her rather prolonged absence. She spat out: "When the cat's away the mice will play!" picked up a solid wooden ruler and, staring daggers at the class, barked: "Put out your hands!" Silence fell like a guillotine blade. I knew, and everybody else knew, what was in store for us. Mrs Wymann, like clock-work, went up and down each aisle striking palms, as if she was swatting flies.

I hated the punishment; for I had not uttered a single word nor had I in any way been delinquent. It was during these moments of injustice that I often thought of the saying "good deeds always get rewarded" and wondered, in my soft juvenile way, if later in life the balance between merit and reward would be tilted and fixed in the same way.

Mrs Armoury, Koo-wie Two, took us twice a week for singing lessons. I had never before seen anyone producing sound from an instrument. Her fingers moving over the ivory keys and the resulting music was nothing short of magic. My favourite song, in Afrikaans, was 'Sari Marais' and, in English, 'John Brown'. I loved the soaring refrain: "But his soul goes marching on". I often wondered who this John Brown was but this was never explained and, since Mrs Wymann was always warning the class that "curiosity killed the cat", I thought it wise not to ask.

I took to school. I liked the new faces, the new surroundings and delighted in the opportunity and the privilege of being near the white teachers, who were so evidently cleaner, cleverer and nobler than the people that lived in the Location.

* * *

Gandhi's tragic death, during my early school years, had made him an instant martyr and a certain saint. Images of him, in print, paint and plaster were visible everywhere. There was a coloured plaster-cast bust of him in 226. It stood incongruously on the sideboard between two brass elephants. It was a private joke of mine to refer to the brass and plaster figures as the G Trio. At School there was a full-length portrait of Gandhi, smiling amiably with his hands leaning on a staff. It hung on the wall that looked down on the stairs running from the first to the ground floor; but it was the Location's way of saying: Gandhi was the cleverest man in the world that really impressed me. How, in heaven's name, I wondered, did they figure that out.

I passed without great challenge through grade one, grade two and standard one. By the end of standard one, however, I was having trouble with my dictation. It wasn't as if the problem was dramatic but I used to confuse there for their, see for sea, fare for fair, faith for fate, too for to, site for sight and a host of other similar words — Mrs Wymann told me that I was having trouble with my homophones.

This was the moment when I most regretted that I wasn't as clever as Gandhi; for I pictured Gandhi, General Smuts, Dr Malan, Churchill, Truman and George VI all seated at a long trestle table writing out a dictation while being closely surveyed by a woman, who curiously looked like Mrs Wymann. The woman, once the dictation was over, asked Smuts, who was sitting at the end, to pass his paper to George VI, who was sitting nearest to the head of the table.

23

She then asked the others to pass their respective dictations to the person sitting immediately to their left. The King passed his paper on to Truman, Truman passed his paper on to Gandhi, Gandhi passed his paper on to Malan, Malan passed his paper on to Churchill, and Churchill passed his paper on to Smuts. The woman then carefully wrote out the dictation on a blackboard and instructed the dictation writers to correct their respective papers. Once the correction was completed, the papers were returned to their owners. Then the woman called out: "No mistakes, stand up!" The only one to do so was Gandhi; and, every time there were subsequent dictations, Gandhi continued to be the only one (except once, when Smuts joined him) to stand up for no mistakes.

5

The Swaraj-Cambridge match that Sunday afternoon, on the Pretoria Indian ground, was typical, one of those early in the season and late in the afternoon matches. The May sun lingered, and was warmer than in June. The curtain-raiser between Stellas and Pretorians was lack-lustre, but I liked Laljit, the tall, quiet and stylish goalkeeper of Pretorians.

My father, when he used to play, stood in the goals for Swaraj. I don't know how it is but parents choose your name, your language, your religion and, without you knowing it, a thousand other things besides. Swaraj was my team. There was not the slightest wish to identify with the six other teams that made up the Pretoria District Football Association.

It was the Location way for us *lightees* to associate ourselves with someone three to five years older than ourselves. These older boys were our mentors and protectors. This practice, never given verbal formulation, was another way of paying respect to seniority, another schooling for that veneration of age that the Location was wont to equate with wisdom.

My mentor, Nithia, was tall, short-tempered, unpredictable and boastful. He had an irritating habit of using long, difficult and unfamiliar words. He never, for instance, said, "I'll try" or "I'm sweating". It was always "I'll endeavour" or "I'm perspiring". He was also said to be a seducer of young, pretty girls. He really knew how to *slaan* a love letter. But when it came to sport he was a washout. He couldn't run for love or money. Kicking a ball, catching a ball and hitting a ball like it should be kicked, caught and hit was for him aspiring to the miraculous; yet that Sunday he was on the ground. He had followed Maga, and I followed him. Maga, Nithia's mentor, was being groomed for a place in Swaraj's first team. The three of us sat on one of the logs that paralleled the long side of the football field. The seating was all on one side: the setting sun, after four o'clock, made watching from the opposite end uncomfortable.

Kick-off was scheduled for three o'clock, but Cambridge asked the referee to spare them a few minutes as their goalkeeper had not turned up. Swaraj raised no objection. One of their players anyway was trying to find a pair of boots which would fit him less tightly than the pair he had already borrowed. It was a good fifteen minutes before the referee blew his whistle.

The match opened at a ding-dong pace. The ball was here, the ball was there, disorder and untidiness was everywhere. Defenders on each side booted the ball high and point blank into their opponents' half, and hoped (this was more like praying than playing) for the best. There was this *dagga-rooker*, Thomas, a Tamil Christian, who used to punt the ball into the air (*appla* it, he used to say) so high that he actually stopped the match for a few seconds while the spectators all looked into the air, as if they were trying to spot some UFO or something. The crowd loved it. It was impressive, magnificent even, but it wasn't football.

The game mysteriously settled down in the second half. The scent of parched grass and chalk rose, while dust swirled about as the stampede of leather-booted feet toed and froed. The spectators, though excited, had remained seated, but now they deserted the low and uncomfortable log seats. The waning sun, from behind, caught their bodies and threw long and thin, Empire-State shadows across the ground.

Swaraj, the younger of the two sides, looked like lasting the hectic pace better than their more senior rivals. Maga, obviously thinking along these lines, told Nithia: "These Cambridge guys are going to start their shit play again — you'll see, Sathia Mia they're going to try and break our boys. They always play like that when they get tired; the fucking bastards!"

Nithia, who knew little about football, greeted the observation with silence, but he nodded and pretended intelligence.

Swaraj's play in the meanwhile had uncannily attained coherence. A volley of swift, short passes were combined with a series of adroit running into open spaces. After twenty minutes, youth and skill told over age and force: Swaraj was leading by three goals to one. Supporters of the winning side buzzed with excited joy. But the mood of the crowd towards the last fifteen minutes of the game became grim. Cheer and joy gave way to bitterness and rage. Tangwell, an ardent Swaraj supporter, choked with recrimination and complained bitterly: "The butchers are trying to cripple our boys!" Turning his head and straining his neck, he addressed the referee with his megaphone voice: "Hey Ref, chuck that dirty Bob off the ground!" Then lowering his voice to conversational pitch, he spoke to a fellow supporter: "The bloody bastards should be in an abattoir, I don't know what the fucking hell they're doing here. I mean this is a fucking football ground, man!"

Bob, the burly Cambridge full back, was the tallest and the broadest of the players on the field. He was like a Primo Carnera let loose among a run of Mickey Rooneys. Off the field, Bob was a nasty brawler. Cambridge, everybody knew, kept him in their side because his Frankenstein physique and dirty tackling terrified opponents. Now, in their dire straits, Bob was using strategy number one to intimidate the Swaraj strikers. His ruse was to harass players, rile them and hurt them until the accumulated provocations forced a rash act of defiance. Then he produced the old Joe Louis. The result was always the same: the opposition, even if there were eleven players on the ground, was reduced to ten or less players.

Now he was trying, with a series of brutal tackles, to intimidate the Swaraj attack. The referee, Alli Barber, a good man but mild and meek, was helpless. To caution Bob too blatantly was to court assault and battery. Still, trying to remain credible, he penalised every one in three of Bob's patent fouls. The Swaraj players, however, arrogant with youth, mocked Bob's intimidating efforts. They needled him with a series of dazzling, long distance dribbles. At last, what from the touch-line seemed inevitable, happened.

27

Bobbye, one of the brilliant young forwards feinted past Bob with Nureyev grace and escaped the obvious, the anticipated foul tackle with ease and disdain. This was a little too much for Mighty Joe Young. Where his boots failed he made good with his fists. *Lousy with his boots, lethal with his fists.* He flattened his young tormentor with a single straight right.

A fracas erupted. The crowd, like a cavalry charge, rushed on to the field. Accusations and blows flew about like sparks. My young heart pounded violently against the insides of my rib cage. The explosion of unrestrained violence and raw words had rent the ordered world of the adults and sent my comprehension reeling into oblivion. My body quaked and my legs trembled. I wanted to flee but Nithia gripped my wrist and, dragging me along, followed Maga. Maga darted through the crowd like a man possessed. I could hear him repeating to himself, as if in a trance, "I'm going to get that bastard! I'm going to get that bastard!"

The bulky movement of leather soles and leather bars kicked up a light dust. A mellow haze formed and clung to the cool, early evening air and began slowly to shroud the quiet grass and the riotous crowd. Visibility, like human decorum, deteriorated. Maga requested something from Nithia. Nithia dug into his trousers pocket and slipped him a tiny object. I spied something shiny and wondered what it was. Maga's looks and expressions, apart from his lividness, gave nothing away.

Violence, like a veld fire, spluttered now here now there. The crowd now surged this way now that way. Some of the spectators tried separating the combatants, others, pretending arbitration, were getting in, whenever and wherever they could, surreptitious blows and kicks. Others, like lonely saints, tried against all odds to restore peace. A few thuggish elements, delighted at this unbecoming outbreak of savagery among the otherwise respectable, shouted with sadistic malice: "Moer hom! Moer hom!"

Maga, ignored by the fighting adults — he was barely sixteen— manoeuvred himself behind Bob. Goliath, frothing at the mouth, was spitting out incoherent and unconvincing words of self-justification. Some among the motley crowd

28

surrounding him, soothed his anger, others stoked it up. Maga, like a shadow, brushed past his rear, and made several sweeping movements across the blue-striped jersey covering his Brooklyn-bridge back. At first, I thought he was making crosses on the Bully's back with some indelible marker. Dark stains, a fraction after he had moved away, spread out on the surface of the jersey like ink on blotting paper. Within seconds Bob was fingering his back. He brought his hand to the front of his face and discovered, with a mixture of raw fear and rank astonishment, that it was covered with fresh blood. In a desperate, panicky movement he pulled the jersey off and asked his team mates to see if he had been stabbed. His friends assured him he hadn't. But though their faces were marked with dismay, they tried to still his anxiety by indicating that he had been extensively but not deeply cut. Bob looked at his blood-stained hand and exclaimed: "Look at that! Look at that! Look at what the fucking cowards have done!"

The injury, so totally unexpected and so flagrantly callous, stung the crowd into a shamed silence. Maga handed back the object to Nithia — it was a razor blade in a metallic holder.

Maga's undiscovered and craven attack drew the afternoon's proceedings to a bleak and abrupt close. Blood, raw and stark, in some mysterious way reminded everyone that football was, after all, just a game. The crowd dispersed and, as darkness fell, the gates of the ground were fastened and bolted behind the last straggling spectator.

6

Autumn was about to end and the new football season had just begun — Swaraj was playing Pirates. How exciting and pleasant I felt that particular Sunday morning. Our house was being renovated from top to bottom: the walls had just been painted and, while they were being allowed to dry, the concrete and enamel sink (in one of the two kitchens) was disconnected and leaned against the wall, right next to the hot and cold water taps. The bright sharp smell of new paint, fresh cement and plaster clung to the air. I recall now that I had just seen, *Yes, Sir, That's My Baby*. Donald O' Connor was the father and the All American football player — I think I must have seen everyone of his Francis (the talking mule) films. I started singing to myself, a passion I acquired without really knowing when or how:

Yes, sir, that's my baby,
No, sir, I don't mean maybe
Yes, sir, that's my baby now.

I returned from the bathroom with an empty metal bucket in my hand. I see myself in the kitchen placing the handle of the bucket over the tap, turning the tap and allowing the hot water to run.

I closed the tap and lifted the bucket and placed it on the floor. Suddenly a sharp grating sound wrung me out of my day-dreaming. I barely had time to realize that the giant slab, with its heavy enamel sink, was bearing down upon me. I lifted my puny arms to protect my head. The edge of the slab, glancing off them and scraping skin away, knocked me down. I found myself flat on the floor, trapped at the thighs

30

and immobilized by the weight of the Moby Dick slab. I felt no pain.

The crash brought my father and brother running into the kitchen. They saw what had happened, tried to hide their anxiety and set out, in total silence, to raise the brutal slab. I was grateful to be released and impatient to be on my feet. I pressed my right foot against the floor and, in an effort to seek leverage, tried to get up. But the leg, like a stick of jelly, flopped about without control. I looked at it with amazement; my brother and father looked on in distress.

In the adjoining room my ailing mother (who suffered from varicose veins) was being attended, as fortune would have it, by Dr Kaplan, an old and benign white doctor. My father, in an unusual fluster, appealed for his help. The doctor entered the kitchen unobtrusively and immediately diagnosed a fracture. A long, wooden spirit-level, with other building tools, occupied a corner of the kitchen. Dr Kaplan used this with a plank of a crate and some bandages to make a splint. I at first wondered at the antics of the doctor but realized that his effort was on my behalf: I felt assured and comforted and proud that I was the centre of all the attention. I was carried and placed on the back seat of my uncle's Dodge car. My uncle, accompanied by my father, then drove me to the Pretoria General Hospital.

The doctors in the emergency ward, after a quick examination, said I was lucky: the slab had neatly split the bone. They smiled and one of them said, "If you're going to break a bone that's the way to do it." Later someone else would say, "The boy was lucky to have had a doctor on hand like that." I, however, thought that "the boy" would have been luckier still if the slab had not moved. The doctors, without any pain-killing drug, tried to reset the bone by pulling at the opposite ends, as if they were at a game of tug-of-war. This gave me my first taste of pain, pure and full. My first night away from 226 was memorably agonizing.

The next day an x-ray photograph revealed that the bone had not, after all, been reset. When I learnt that I would have to be the rope of another tug-of-war, I shuddered. But then, to my relief, I learnt that this time I was destined for the

31

operating theatre, where, under chloroform — though no surgery would be performed — the bone would be reset and my leg would be replastered.

My father visited me on the morning of the operation.

"Did you have your operation, already?"

I felt drowsy and saw my father as through a dream. "No," I answered.

"Have you been to the operation room?"

"Yes."

I remembered my bed being pushed into a huge room and I recalled the tiled white walls being formidably festooned with nickeled slitting and snipping instruments, white doctors and nurses in masks; a black rubber cup-like instrument being put over my mouth and nose, and a doctor requesting me to take a deep breath.

My father smiled.

* * *

I slept well that evening and every evening after that. The hospital, the Cassim Adam Ward, room 12 (which contained one other bed) became my new home. My right leg was strapped from thigh to ankle, lifted and held in suspension by a pulley. I was bed-ridden and condemned to a single sleeping position.

I insisted on being visited every day, twice a day. Once in the afternoon, after lunch, and once in the evening, after supper. My father, throughout the three-and-a-half months, came to visit me in the afternoon. In the evenings my mother came, with someone willing to drive her to the hospital in the Chevrolet truck that my father then owned.

I shared number 12, during the first week, with an old Christian Tamil man who came from Claremont, an outlying Pretoria area. The man told me that he was recovering from an appendicitis operation. Then I had a five-year old Chinese patient with me. I recognised the patient's parents: they had a shop in Barber Street, near the football grounds. The African nurse, whose confidence I had won, explained, just before the tiny patient was moved into number 12, that he had to have a tube put into his stomach because he wasn't able to go to the toilet like other children. But the poor child didn't stay long: the equipment his treatment required became too cumbersome for a shared room. My third partner was David Fischer from Lady Selborne, another outlying Pretoria area. David, though one of his arms was in a sling, was happy, helpful and self-sufficient; he was about the same age as my brother. He puzzled me: what was this happy-go-lucky character, so at odds with the sick odour of chlorine and disinfectant, and the unhappy sight of helpless and broken bodies, doing here?

When we knew each other better, I asked him, how come he was in hospital.

"Oh, I had an accident. My brother's motor bike, a Norton, was in the back yard. I had a go at it when nobody was around. The fucking thing went off like a stone from a catty right into a bloody barbed wire fence. The benchot wire got me here."

He took off the sling and showed me his upper arm. The unexpected sight of tender, unevenly mended tissue in a deep hollow where a biceps muscle should have been made me feel queasy. I vainly groped for a word of sympathy but my search and discomfort was cut short when David said: "Ag, alles sal reg kom. Jy weet ... you know, they're taking from here to put here."

He indicated with his left hand, in a sort of Charlie Chaplin gesture, that the doctors were going to take flesh from his buttocks and transfer it to his damaged biceps.

"And you man, how did you get yourself into such a deurmekaar?" He lightly tugged at the weights, smiled and simulated a vicious glee as my leg rose a fraction. I acknowledged his prank with a fake expression of pain and then told him of my own accident. When David learnt that I had already spent three weeks in hospital, he said: "Ek sê, it's a pity you're not in the States; hulle is so slim daar — they would have had you fixed up in two weeks." His eyes twinkled, as if he was saying to himself: I bet you didn't know that? He turned away and made for the door. He left the room, whistling Teresa Brewer's 'Music! Music! Music!'

33

Two weeks? A mental-made movie, featuring, in techni-colour, Jarman shoes, McGregor lumber jackets, the *Esquire* magazine, the Empire State Building and my uncle's Dodge car crackled and jumped on the liquid screen of my mind. Then I saw myself up and about; and playing a little football already — I regretted that I wasn't an American or that I did not have a father rich enough to take me to the States. But it was near eight o'clock. My thoughts turned away from this happy reflection as I switched on my bedside Pye radio and tuned into my favourite program, 'Consider Your Verdict'.

The radio and comics comforted me during the fourteen-week stay away from 226. I listened regularly to Radio Play House, Saturday afternoon sport programs (I closely followed the matches of Newcastle United, who were touring the country just then) and 'The Scarlet Pimpernel' — I loved the jingle which announced the serial:

They seek him here,
They seek him there.
Those damned ol' Frenchies seek him everywhere.
Is he in heaven?
Or is in hell?
That damned ol' Scarlet Pimpernel;

I received a pile of comics from the family and well-wish-ers. I read the Mutt and Jeff ones as soon as they came to hand, and, within weeks, accumulated an impressive num-ber of them on my metal bedside table.

My room, always spotlessly clean, gave on to the little-used car park, but my bed was on the far side of the window. The soft, rhythmic chants of hymn singing, emanating from where I had no idea, pervaded the room with grace and gave sound the smell of incense. The light outside, the holy blue of the sky, the vibrant sounds of the chirping birds all some-how seemed different. Was it due, I reflected, to the young white priest, dressed in a black cassock, who came bearing a

34

friendly smile and dispensing encouragement and unsolicited blessings, or was it the custard and raspberry jelly the kitchen staff served for dessert that made the difference. Whatever it was, it evoked the mystery and magic of Sunday, and I felt it as unmistakably, as if I was back in Jerusalem Street.

On Sundays too the ward, after lunch, buzzed with visitors — it seemed, as if the people who had in the morning been to the cemetery now in the afternoon came to the hospital. On one occasion, while I was waiting for my parents to show up, an under forty Muslim couple — probably from Prinsloo Street, where many of the merchant Memons lived and traded — entered number 12. The woman, taking pity on me and thinking I was also a Muslim, addressed me in Gujarati, which was, of course, all Greek to me. When I explained that I was neither Muslim nor Gujarati they felt embarrassed but wished me well all the same. The man left saying, "God is great!" These words, a conundrum, if ever there was one, had been addressed to me before. I recalled once, when I had explained to a total stranger how I had received my injury, the stranger immediately rounded off my report with the condolence, "God is great!"

I kept wondering about these words. What, I asked myself, has the greatness of God got to do with my mishap. I turned them over in my mind. God, obviously, was being praised, but were they really praising him for sending *me* to hospital. Perhaps, they thought I was lucky to be in hospital. Again I was tempted to ask someone about these odd words but I didn't think my parents would be able to deal with them. I regretted the absence of Jopa.

After twelve weeks, my leg was freed. At last, I could have the sheet and blanket covering me as they were meant to cover me; at last, I was relieved from the bedsores that had plagued me ever since the third week — at last, I could use the bedpan seated on both my bottoms.

From the start I was urged by Doctor Hertzog (a friendly though stern-looking Afrikaner) to move and wriggle my toes as much as possible. Each time he visited, which was at least once a week, he asked if I felt any pain. If I answered negatively, he would ask me to move my exposed toes. Then he measured my progress by the vigour and dexterity I displayed in their movement.

Two days after the leg had been released, the staff nurse, Sister Armstrong, a mannish woman, who was the terror of the ward, feared by nurses, patients and visitors alike, came to inspect my progress. When she witnessed the enthusiasm and the exuberance manifested by the injured leg's toes, she lifted me out of bed and swept me out of the room, like Tarzan carrying Jane, and into the rear end of the ward, where there was a terraced verandah beautifully exposed to the sun. She let me down into a deck-like chair, placed a blanket, which she had recovered from a corridor cupboard, on the polished cement floor and then placed me on the blanket.

7

I can see why they didn't want us to see *Island in the Sun*,
Harry Belafonte goes out with Joan Fontaine; *No Way Out*,
Sidney Poitier is the cop and Richard Widmark is the robber;
Blackboard Jungle, Sidney Poitier is the good student and
Glenn Ford is his teacher friend; *Something of Value*, Sidney
Poitier and Rock Hudson are boyhood friends; *The Defiant
Ones*, Sidney Poitier is chained to Tony Curtis; *Porgy and
Bess*, too many blacks; *Lilies of the Field*, Sidney Poitier
obtained an academy award. But why was *Gone with the
Wind* with Clark Gable and Vivien Leigh; *A Street Car
Named Desire*, with Marlon Brando and Vivien Leigh; *The
Days of Wine and Roses*, with Jack Lemmon and Lee
Remick; *Somebody Up There Likes Me* with Paul Newman,
banned for us. Even now I see that Ocean's eleven poster
outside the Royal cinema with a black swathe painted across
Sammy Davis, Jr, because he was the only black among the
Sinatra clan. And why, oh why, was *Rebel Without a Cause*,
and *East of Eden*, the James Dean films, banned for us. I
remember I saw those films through Patrick Jackson's
description of them — the Chinese for some reason could
attend the all-white cinemas.

I have among my photos a picture of Patrick that I took
with my Voightlander camera. I see him now with a leather
lumber jacket. Was he trying to look like James Dean? If he
was, he certainly succeeded; if he wasn't he was lucky and
he didn't know it. No, on second thoughts, he was unlucky:
people (white and black) didn't expect a Chinese to look like
James Dean — such things were simply not done; so no one
really noticed, and he never referred to it. Perhaps he didn't
know — or did he?

I met Patrick Jackson, a Chinese from Canton, after my accident and long convalescence when I returned to school again, and began where I had left off, that is, in standard two. I remember that first play-time break on that first morning because Patrick addressed me: "Are you scared of me?"

Why, I wondered, this hostile question out of the blue like that. I looked into the older Chinese boy's face, a clear-skinned, sharp-featured face, and said, without fear or bravado, "No."

"OK, let's fight then!"

"Fight? What do you mean fight?"

"Well, if you're not scared of me, we must fight to see who is stronger."

I smiled, for his logic surprised and amused me and yet I wasn't intimidated. Although I had never been involved in a physical fight before, I was, naively without doubt, sincere when I had said, I wasn't scared of him. So I said courteously: "No, I'm not scared of you but I don't see any reason why we should fight. I don't have any quarrel with you." My words or perhaps my innocence impressed him; for from that day on we became friends.

Patrick shared a desk with his cousin Dennis Howling, who was tall, wavy-haired and slightly feminine-looking. It was just a matter of time before the friendship I enjoyed with Patrick extended to Dennis. Neelen Daramalingam (his mother was Malay and his father was Tamil) and Ebrahim (Ebies) Mohamed, lively and non-conformist characters, slowly gravitated towards the three of us and pretty soon, without anybody being aware of it, we metamorphosed into a clan of five.

Mister Freen, an ex-serviceman, nearing retirement, was our teacher. He suffered visibly from shell-shock. He spoke a little Tswana and seemed to have quite an open mind, but I was glad to see the year with him go by quickly: I felt we were out on a limb in that *madressa* — the classroom had seen better days as a large corner shop. The venues of the various and scattered vernacular schools had become part of the Pretoria Boys' School. I was pleased when, for standard three, we returned to School proper. I was a little less enthusiastic about having Mrs Armoury (Koo-wie Two) but I soon discovered that she never used, though she was very strict, the arbitrary method of punishment so dear to Mrs Wymann.

I took to all the subjects, but history and English were my favourites. I was stirred by the story of Wolraad Woltemade, the eighteenth-century farmer who sacrificed his life, and the life of his horse, to rescue victims of a wreck near Cape Town; shocked by the dastardly deeds of Dingaan, the Zulu Chief; moved by the valour and martyrdom of Piet Retief, the Trek leader; thrilled by the six-hundred-mile horse ride of Dick King, the British cavalry officer; and disenchanted with the busy-body activities of Dr John Philip, the inspector of the London Missionary Society.

During the English lessons I livened to the knowledge and the realization of what a simile, a metaphor, a euphemism, a hyperbole, a climax, an anti-climax and a personification were; but I loved most of all the last fifteen minutes of each day when Mrs Armoury read from Enid Blyton and made the Famous Five: Julian, Dick, George, Anne and their dog, Timmy, come alive in the classroom.

* * *

Patrick impressed me with his handling of pencil and brush. To me, making paper come alive with trees and streams, and with horses and houses was — like making music from ivory — pure magic. Patrick finished his copy of a picture — one that he had been steadily working on for some time. Everybody, including Mrs Armoury, was awed by his drawing prowess. I looked at the picture of a shipwreck pinned to the wall and the drawing he had made of it. The only difference, I could detect, was in the colours — ship, sky and sea, worn and faded in the picture, were fresh and bright in the drawing.

Mrs Armoury was so impressed that she left the class to request the presence of Mr Caulineck, the principal. Dennis was her monitor; so she instructed him before leaving: "If anybody misbehaves, Dennis, you just put his name on the board and he'll get the punishment he deserves." Then, turning to the rest of the class, she said: "Now, you behave yourselves! I'm going to fetch the Principal and when I get back, I don't want to see (pointing to the blackboard) a single name on that board."

Dennis loved the job of being a policeman. Noor Mohamed, an incorrigible talker and fidget, true to form, had his name written on the board within the first two minutes.

"Ah, Dennis, have a heart. I was only asking Carim for a rubber."

"No talking, I said!" Dennis simulated severity.

"Ag, please Dennis, give a guy a last chance!"

"I said no talking, Noor!"

"Just one chance, asseblief Baas."

Dennis turned around and neatly wrote Noor's name on the board for a second time. A reinforced silence fell over the class until somebody made an exaggerated farting sound. Dennis's face flushed red.

"Who did that?"

"WHO — DID — THAT?"

Silence.

I knew Patrick was the culprit. I also knew Dennis wouldn't write his name or the names of any of the clan on the board. Dennis surveyed the class, row after row and face after face, and then repeated, what by now was more of a plea than a command: "Who did that?"

Patrick lackadaisically said, "I think, it's Sattar Aboobaker." The class greeted the information with a roar of laughter — Sattar was the quietest, the most undaring and the most conforming member of the class. Dennis, trying to suppress his own laughter, gave up and joined the general hilarity and heartiness.

Suddenly he grew serious and anxious. Silence once again fell over the class. He instructed Neelen to climb on to one of the desks and to peer out of one of the three highly placed windows. A minute later, Neelen called out: "Arra, they're coming!" Dennis quickly wiped Noor's name off the board.

Mr Caulineck, a thin, bespectacled figure, scrutinised the drawing. His call, in this way, was rare and exceptional. He

40

praised Patrick for his adroitness and went on to say, with that whistling rasp his voice had, that the drawing was not "original." A real artist, he said, creates and doesn't copy. Most of the class, intimidated by his presence, listened in dumb silence. To me this was a reproach and I looked at Patrick and wondered if he had sensed it in the same way.

"You see, the greatness of the European resides in his ability to create. Leonardo di Vinci and Michelangelo were true artists because they were creators and creation is the true test of intelligence. That is why the Natives in our country are where they are to-day — they lack the spirit of creativity."

Noor Mohamed fidgeted. Mr Caulineck used his ice-blue eyes to clip Noor over the ears. He then cleared his throat while adjusting his steel-rimmed spectacles and continued: "I'll give you an example. Take the Zulus, for instance, now, you know, when we count we progress from ten to twenty, and from twenty to thirty and so on; when the Zulus have to count ten plus ten they do not say twenty, they say ten ten; and when they have to count twenty plus ten, they do not say thirty, they say: ten ten ten — which is a clear indication of their inability to create."

He moved towards Mrs Armoury, exchanged a few words and then left urging the class to keep up the good work and reminding us not to forget to create.

8

Patrick and I shared a desk in standard six and for the first time girls and boys were in the same class. The old Girls' School became a junior school and the Boys' School became a mixed high school: the Pretoria Indian High School. There were four rows of twin wooden desks in the classroom: the girls occupied the two rows closest to the door that gave on to the corridor, and the boys occupied the two rows closest to the window that overlooked a small lawn, a hedge and, in the distance, two prefab classrooms.

I was pleased to get away from Mrs Armoury. It's not that I didn't like her, but three consecutive years with the same teacher, in the same prefab, was more than monotonous. After all (I had heard it said so many times), variety was the spice of life. Besides, it was good to be in the main building — there was something second class about the prefabs — even though the class, as first year high school pupils, were confined to the ground floor. And it was also new and exciting to have different teachers for different subjects: Mrs Botha for English; Mrs Van der Walt for Afrikaans; Mr Van Dyk, an amiable Hollander with imperfect English and a pronounced Dutch accent, for arithmetic and bookkeeping; Mr Strauss, an eccentric German, for physical science and geography; Mrs Dougall, a grave old Canadian, for biology; Mr Soma, the only Indian teacher among them, for history; and Mr Freen for race studies, a subject not previously taught in school.

I remember the first race-studies lesson because Mr Caulineck was there and he addressed the class: "As you know, you now start a new year. Being the 'A' section of standard six we expect many of you to reach standard ten,

42

and some of you to obtain Matric Certificates. I am here today to welcome you; to urge you to work hard — as you did under Mrs Armoury — and to warn you that you are now in the senior league and that there is no place for shirkers and idlers.

"However, I am here, above all, to introduce you to a new subject. The educational authorities esteem that South Africa is a country of many races and deem it wise therefore that we should devote some of our study time to the question of race. Mr Freen, whom some of you have had in standard two, and I am sure you are aware has travelled widely and who has several languages at his command, will be your race studies teacher.

"We don't as yet have any textbook, which means we will have to manage, for the moment, as best we can. The primary problem of race in South Africa is how are the different peoples, with different levels of civilisation, to live together. It has taken the European two thousand years to reach his present level of civilisation: we cannot expect the Native, whose level of civilisation is still juvenile, to effect the same progress in less time. There may be, besides, an additional reason why the Native will never be the equal of the European; I have here a book, *Day Dawn in South Africa*. It is written by one of South Africa's foremost historians and this is what he states:

Science is only now gradually discovering the remarkable physiological differences between the brain of the white man of European descent and that of the Bantu — differences which are innate and constitute the measure of their respective intellectual capacities ...

Today science brings us proofs that the cerebral capacities of what we conveniently call "native," are, when he has reached the age of puberty, distinctly inferior in comparison with those of the white children of a civilisation of 2,000 years. We know now that many of the ganglion cells of the native's brain remain undeveloped; and we know, with some degree of certainty, that his intellectual development — which before the age of puberty is more or less comparable with that of a normal white child — comes to a standstill, as if it were not capable of further development.

43

"And on that note — which will give you food for thought — I leave you in the capable hands of Mr Freen."

Was this, I ruminated, the answer to the anguish over my careless remark to Blackie? Was this the answer to the great South African riddle. Mr Freen cut short my meditation when he started talking about the head measurements of the different races, mentioning odd, new and difficult sounding words like: dolichocephalic, mesocephalic and brachycephalic; and the names of the different races: Mongoloids, Caucasoids and Negroids. Later, he went on to mention someone called Mendel but it was the last period of the day: my concentration flagged and the heat of the past-noon sun made me feel drowsy — I had to fight off sleep until I was saved by the bell.

Race studies, however, didn't last long; for Mr Freen became ill and he wasn't replaced. The last period on Tuesday afternoons became a library hour.

In the library I sought out the big illustrated books. There was nothing on football, the American cinema or clothes; so I settled for books with titles like: *Heroes of Science*, *Famous Men of America*, *The Bible Lands*, *The Wonders of the World* and *The Capitals of Europe*.

I liked the physical science and geography periods because I liked Mr Strauss. During one of his lessons Mr Strauss walked up to the light switch, put the light on and, pointing to the illuminated ceiling lamp, urged: "Never be content with just switching the light on, ask yourself (pointing to the ceiling and then to the switch) why does that light up when I switch this on; for why is the beginning of all knowledge and all learning." I was impressed because the spirit of what the teacher had said was so opposite to that of the Location.

When, a few days later, I was about to set off for school, I saw my mother introducing chunks of dry cow dung into a bucket of water and then mixing it with her bare hands. An old African (on a rickety cart drawn by a scrawny horse) went about the Location selling pails of dried cow dung to the various houses. I knew my mother had already swept the sand pavement in front of the house and I knew she was

44

going to go out and sprinkle the liquid dung over the swept portion of the pavement but the sight of her mixing the stuff with her bare hands, although it wasn't the first time I had seen her doing that, disconcerted me. Now, with Mr Strauss' encouragement, I asked her point blank: why was she doing something so *naar*.

"When I was a small girl I saw my mother do it. Now I do it. What was good enough for my mother, is good enough for me."

"Yes, but why did she do it?"

"Ah, that's a question you should have asked her."

That, of course, was her polite way of telling me to leave her alone; for my maternal grandmother had died long before I was born.

I've often wished that I had the power to question the dead. I recall the photo in my parents' bedroom, where my maternal grandmother and Jopa were attending the wedding of some close relatives. She must have been very young then — she certainly looked very young — for Jopa, sitting next to her, was carrying a tiny tot on his knees: my mother.

I tried to imagine how that slim, sharp-featured, strikingly handsome woman (the very opposite of how I imagined a grandmother to be) would have answered my question. Maybe she would have smiled softly — she had that fragile and breakable look written all over her face — and would have said sweetly: "I don't know. I saw my mother do it; so now I do it." In the Location you never got a real answer to a real question.

* * *

I was sixteen then and beginning to savour the feeling of independence. I remember how at the end of each term we were given our exam results on a progress card. If you had under forty per cent in any subject the mark was circled in red. You had to take the progress card home and have it signed by your parents and then have it returned to the class teacher. Since I knew my parents wouldn't understand its significance and since I was afraid that it would, more than anything else, cause them embarrassment, I decided to sign it myself. I made no attempt to copy my father's signature; I simply wrote out his name clean and clear. From that day on I became responsible — solely responsible — for my card and for my education. How simple and straightforward everything seemed then.

Our Afrikaans teacher, Mrs Van der Walt, was everything I imagined a white woman to be: fleshy, leggy, beautiful, clean, immaculate, perfumed and painted — lips, fingers and toes. Later, when I saw the British actress Kay Kendall in *Doctor in the House*, I saw Mrs Van der Walt. She had the reputation of being severe: it wasn't physical punishment she doled out but lines — a minor delinquency got you a hundred lines; a major one, five hundred.

My attitude to Afrikaans was, in many ways, like my attitude to Tamil. My mind, as if it was a door-keeper, treated both as potential gatecrashers. Tamil, as far as I could see, was anachronistic and the manifestation of pure nostalgia.

I remember one day I was in the new kitchen poking fun at Tamil by turning familiar words upside down and inside out, slurring my accent, exaggerating my hand expressions and generally cocking a snook at Tamil decorum. My mother and sisters found my linguistic antics hilarious. My father came in just in time to catch the tail end of my performance. He was not amused. He fixed me with a chilly stare and said, icily: "If you can't speak our language without mocking it, it is better not to speak it at all!"

Deep ethnocentric emotion, I sensed, was at play. I was unintentionally offending the tribal God. I heeded the stricture with total fidelity. I never thereafter uttered another Tamil sentence, although it was quite impossible to get along without certain Tamil words. There is, for instance, no real English or European equivalent of *cowchie* to indicate that unpleasant smell left by meat or egg improperly spiced or cooked, or by cutlery improperly washed; nothing in English or Afrikaans to match the vivid *katcha-mootcha* that my mother was always using to castigate the sight of disorder or rank untidiness; and nothing to equal the implied contempt in *malacotta* for people who were vulgar in behavior and appearance.

46

As for Afrikaans, my dislike of the language was undoubtedly inspired by my Saturday presence at the Market. It had become a habit, since recovering from my accident, to help my father on Saturdays — retail trade on that day was brisk. I earned a little pocket money and got a chance to see other white people, but the Market also had its drawbacks; for more than one white woman would make it obvious that she didn't want to touch my hand when paying for the fruit or vegetables she had just bought; and more than once I was carelessly called "Sam" or *Coolie* or *Charra*.

I noticed that this racial haughtiness was absent in the behaviour of the overseas whites. Through them (and through the cinema — I remembered *Cimarron*, where Glenn Ford defends the rights of a Red Indian) I was won to the conviction that racialism was foreign to England, unknown on the Continent and exclusive to the Afrikaners. Confirmation for this came with a lone incident.

Praga and Boya, Uncle Rajee's sons, worked for an Italian called Gastaldi. Gastaldi's stall was next door to my father's. During the quiet periods of the day my cousins and I got together and wiled away the time by talking about football, films, clothes and white women; although most of the time we just indulged in nonsense talk; that is (to call it what the Location would have called it), shit talk.

One day I noticed two young white girls eyeing Praga. He was tall and good-looking. The two mature teenagers, seeing him in front of Gastaldi's stall, mistook him for a bronzed Italian. He couldn't hear them but they were obviously, in low voices, discussing his physical features. I imagined, from the looks they were giving him, that they were saying something like: "Golly, just look at those eye lashes, really like a doll's or Isn't he handsome?" or "Gee, he sure is swell!" But a minute later, when he was within earshot and when they had discovered he wasn't Italian, he heard one of them, mixing disappointment with contempt, say: "Ag, hy's net n' koolie."

Afrikaans, to my mind, represented not only injustice but also coarseness and brutality. How could anyone black or brown, I kept asking myself, accept a system of words that

47

embodied our very own humiliation. I consequently kept, during Afrikaans lessons, a low profile. I never ventured to put my hand up, never volunteered to answer a question and never showed my work unless it was absolutely necessary. But this loathing for Afrikaans didn't prevent me from keeping a circumspect but sharp eye on Mrs Van der Walt's legs. The supreme pleasure, when she crossed her legs — which she did from time to time — was to catch a glimpse of that discretion and ultimate mystery, her underwear. But her movements were ever so soft and ever so discreet: she never spread her legs out, never opened them, never crossed them, never, that is, carelessly. My watch was never rewarded.

The next best thing I wanted to do was to touch her hand, to touch those soft, sensually magnificent hands — to touch them just once. But I was convinced it was a vain hope; for even when I took my book up to her table to be marked, I had to, like all the others, approach, put the open notebook on the table, indicate where the piece of work that required marking began and then step back a nice distance. I was taught (and so was everyone else) to respect this particular code of behaviour very early in my schooling.

On one occasion she gave us a letter to write — a letter to a friend. The task was to explain how the last holiday was spent. It was the first time she had given us a full assignment. About this time also I had quite given up the idea of ever touching her hand and of ever attracting her attention; for she hadn't as yet noticed me and she didn't even know my name and she wouldn't even have been able — if, for instance she had met me in the play ground or in the corridor — to vouch that I belonged to one of her classes. My Afrikaans was correct but not anything to boast about. I knew I had no chance of impressing her that way. I took extra care therefore to get the form of the letter right. I respected all the spacing and punctuation norms that went with the beginning and the end of a letter, the address, the titles and the various abbreviations. I also made sure that my work had no smudges, blots, scratches or rubbing outs. At the end of the lesson she instructed her monitor, Tracy, a half-"Coloured" half-Indian girl, to collect the work in for

48

her. I felt satisfied that I had done enough, at least not to be rebuked. I knew perfectly well that I wasn't going to love Afrikaans even for Mrs Van der Walt.

A week later she had marked the work and had the pile of books on the top of her table ready to hand out. She picked up the first notebook and enquired: "Who is J — Jay Naidoo?"

When I heard the name, my Adam's apple dropped into my shoes. God, what had I done. Had I misunderstood what she had asked us to do. I timidly lifted my hand. She swept towards me and said, stretching her hand out: "Let me shake your hand!" I glanced at Patrick and then shot my hand out. She grasped it and pressured my hand more than I did hers. Her hand was exactly as I had imagined it to be: warm, soft and silky smooth. But the pleasure of her touch was oh, so brief. Still swirling in the mystery of her action, I saw her turn and walk back to her table. I just had time enough to admire her hour-glass shape before she placed herself on the platform next to the table.

"He is the one person in this class who understands that cleanliness is second to godliness!" She opened my book and displayed it to the class. It was difficult for most to see what she was getting at but, in her mind, the double pages that contained my letter were spotless. She then lifted a second book belonging to Haroun Mohamed, which, in contrast, was a smudgy disaster. The class burst out in laughter. Poor Haroun, he had already acquired the reputation of being untidy with Mrs Armoury and she had vainly tried to correct his failing. Mrs Van der Walt, the class understood, wasn't going to change that then. But it was thanks to Haroun that I now possessed the hand — the only hand in the class and, perhaps, in the School — that had touched the hand of Mrs Van der Walt.

9

One fine January afternoon, Patrick, Innie and I took a walk into town. We bought some delicious home-made ice-cream from the Trambridge Café, which was near the Caledonian Stadium. We wanted to sit down in a quiet spot and just linger awhile. Burgers Park was nearby but out of bounds. Innie — elegant like his dandy, Tamil father and light-skinned, querulous and truculent like his half-"Coloured" and half-African mother — said it was going on for four o'clock and we'd be wise to make our way home. He pointed to the lengthening shadows of the plane-trees.

The walk was pleasant and, as was so often the case, the familiar but foreign surroundings turned our talk to the privileges we saw all around us: spacious houses, well-kept flats, quiet and abundant boarding houses, smart and functional hotels, office blocks and cinemas; cool and verdant parks, austere and quaint churches and many inviting and sumptuous cafes. It was Innie who said: "Yessus man, these laanies have all the luck. Imagine being able to live in the centre of town in one of these houses or flats!"

I remember that I didn't mind the houses or the flats, or any of the other privileges that the whites had cornered for themselves; but I did mind that we couldn't sit down in the café that had sold us the ice-creams, or sit down and have a cup of tea or coffee in any one of the many other cafes we came across; and I found it insufferably unfair and mean that we couldn't enter the parks and sit on the grass or on the benches.

Patrick, unexpectedly, quipped: "Oh, in this bloody country, if you're not white, there's only one of two things to do: become a saboteur or run fafi."

Innie and I burst out laughing. Patrick looked at us and smiled wryly.

We came to the corner of Bosman and Pretorius Streets. We passed just in front of Ralph and Clary's, the American-owned café, where one-foot long hot dogs, freshly fried doughnuts and white bread, already sliced and wrapped in attractive grease paper, were sold. I vicariously felt the presence of America in my belly. The robot turned green and we nonchalantly crossed the street. Three white men, young, strong and athletic, traversed from the opposite end. One of them, in a deliberate show of bravado, menaced Innie with his shoulder. Innie stood his ground. There was a sharp short shock. Patrick, being on the far side of the clash, hardly noticed. I looked at Innie and winked approval.

When we reached the pavement we turned, almost simultaneously, to look back; and, as it happened, the three whites did the same. Silent signals of contempt were mutually transmitted. Then we continued homewards. Later Innie and I discovered that our white antagonists had turned around and, though they tried to hide their intention, were making an effort to catch up with us.I noticed they were dressed identically: khaki elastic-topped short pants, khaki socks — worn up to the knees like footballers — and white, short-sleeved, glad-necked shirts. They had amazon faces. One was freckled and sported a crew-cut hairstyle, which was then the fashion among the backveld whites.

The three whites overtook us, turned around and squared up to us. They directed their hostility towards Innie. Demonstrating solidarity, I closed in on his side. My gesture wasn't pure bravery; for I instinctively realized that we had to stick together but the real reason I felt no fear was the presence of Patrick. Patrick, I told myself, wouldn't be neutral; he knew more about fighting than either Innie or I did and, what is more, reputations of toughness didn't intimidate him. My action, obvious and deliberate, deflected the hostility of our white adversaries. The biggest of them, his blue eyes cold and full of hate, ignored Innie, came straight up to me and spat out, in Afrikaans: "So you think you're tough?"

The muscles on my jaw tightened. I looked into my white

51

opponent's eyes. The white youth shot out a blow to my head. I anticipated it and avoided it by drawing back. The white youth then took up a boxing stance and came at me. Cars and trucks whirred past; their movements made the trunks of the Jacaranda trees on both sides of the street flash and for a fraction of a second I felt as if I was on a train. Seventeen-and-a-half years had cautioned me to realize that I couldn't, in full daylight and in the centre of Oom Paul's town, think of striking a white man. Yet strange enough, I wasn't afraid. I expected Patrick to step in and to tell my aggressor: "Hey, if you know what's good for you, you'd better cut it out!" But Patrick didn't budge; Innie didn't budge and the allies of our white foe didn't budge either.

My antagonist aimed another blow to my head. I dodged it and struck back, not to hurt but to discourage. My light blow glanced off the white youth's shoulder. Suddenly a kaleidoscope of movement and curses (in Afrikaans) enveloped us. Two uniformed white policemen, with their holstered 38 Smith and Westons and their nickled handcuffs jangling and dangling from their belts, appeared as if from nowhere, and bundled us off the pavement and into a huge brick building.

What's this? I wondered and looked around, and suddenly realized that we had been just outside the main police station. The three whites were led away. I looked around and saw that we were in the non-European side of the charge office. The white policeman behind the counter — he couldn't have been more than twenty — bawled out in Afrikaans: "And what's this now, fighting with a white man? Where do you think you are, hey?"

I said (in Afrikaans) that I was merely trying to defend myself.

"What's your name?" I gave him my name. My two friends stood silently aside. The policeman ignored them. I provided further details: address and my account of what had happened. After noting down everything the policeman warned me: next time there would be no trifling with the gesture of fighting a white man in the street, no matter what the reason. I replied with a silent stare: "That'll be day!"

52

We left the station. Outside Innie and Patrick got excited. Patrick hadn't really understood how the "fight" had started. Innie, almost beside himself with excitement, provided the bare details. Then they both asked me about the fight. This puzzled me, for they were both present and were as aware of what had happened as I was. I tried to explain that nothing, in effect, had taken place — there was only the semblance of a fight. But I couldn't dissuade them.

I soon forgot the incident. Three weeks later on my way back from School, I noticed a strange Ford car outside 226. When I approached the porch of the house, I saw, just beyond the entrance and on the side of one of the two walnut arm-chairs (the front door was always wide open during the day time) a police officer's cap lying on the maroon carpet. I wondered what was happening. As I approached within touching distance of the door, I saw my father seated in the other arm-chair: the welling anxiety subsided. Once inside the sitting room I saw three white policemen. Two were seated on the sofa and one, whose cap I had noticed, was seated (opposite my father) in the armchair behind the open door.

"These men want to talk to you, Jay."

I looked at the policemen, wondering what, in heaven's name, I could have done. The one in the armchair spoke. He was obviously senior to the other two and, now that I had a closer look at him, I could see he was also older. He had a square benign face and sported a slightly greying moustache. He spoke in English.

"Are you Jay Naidoo?"

"Yes."

"Do you remember having a fight with a white person in Pretorius Street on Tuesday, 28 January 1958, at 4.10 p.m.?"

The incident came back at once. "Yes," I replied.

"In your statement to the police, you claim that the white person, accompanied by two other persons, accosted you and then tried to assault you. Is that correct?"

"Yes."

"You see, these three white chappies were police recruits. And police regulations strictly forbid such confrontations with members of the public."

I wanted to smile when I heard the words "members of the public" but I managed a straight face.

"Would you like to press charges against them?"

It was the Location tradition not to become legally entangled with whites; it was an even greater tradition, not to contest the white man's superiority. If he insulted you, you swallowed your pride; if you asked him — even if he was a public servant — to help you, you supplicated and grovelled: *Ja baas, nee baas, ekskuus baas, asseblief baas, dankie baas*. It made me sick. I declined his offer.

The police officer said nothing further. The visitors bid me and my father good day and left. Father remained silent and watched the whole proceeding as a remote observer. I detected that there was, even so, a gleam of pride in his eyes.

10

How I wished I could have forsaken the Tamil language. Why couldn't I, like the "Coloured" boys and girls, stay at home after school, go to the cinema or just play outside. Why did School have to be followed by another school. I hated Tamil School. I hated the foreignness it suggested; hated the alienness it inspired; hated the nonsense it perpetuated; hated the makeshift and derisory character of its instruction. In English school learning (arithmetic, geography, history, nature study, hygiene, English and Afrikaans) was exacting and exciting; in Tamil School learning was the five R's: rote, reading, writing and wretched repetition.

I remembered little of my first year there except that I had to trace over, countless times, the first letter of the Tamil alphabet (aa-na) — the teacher neatly wrote it out, in giant form, on each and every pupil's slate.

A few years later, as I recollect, I stood at the edge of the stoep of 226 and looked past the towering eucalyptus tree. Slightly to the right my eyes picked out the reddish-grey ornamental structure piercing the clear blue sky like a spear's head. I stared blankly into space and cursed: "Bloody Tammy!"

I felt the quiet warmth of winter as I crossed the street and walked on towards the corner of Jerusalem and Blood Streets. My eyes, following the unenthusiastic movement of my feet, fell upon a half-hidden shiny object. Was it a tickey? I stooped to pick it up but before my hand reached it I realized that it was just a *pannakie*.

"Hey, what are you up to? Have you lost something?"

It was the unmistakable voice of Uncle Anand, my mother's younger brother. I looked up and saw him standing outside Abdul Supplies Store and waiting for a customer to turn up; it was his wont to tease me in this way. I gave him a don't-bother-me look.

"What's up Jay? You don't look so good today, boy! Aren't you on your way to the eyesee?"

"Ag, you know perfectly well that I've got to go to Tammy!"

"Ah, yes. Well, hard luck, you won't be able to see *Bud Abbott and Lou Costello Meet Frankenstein*."

I, who from the age of six had seen at least two American films a week, was going to tell him it was *Abbot and Costello Meet the Killer* but just then one of the doors of the eating house, on the "Coloured" side of the corner, opened from inside and out wafted the rich, earthy smell of stew and pap. I regretted not having found the tickey: I was really longing for some *barebies*.

I passed Uncle Rajee's house that adjoined the store and approached the corner of Fifth and Blood Streets. I hoped Sawmiss wasn't there, for he was another one like Uncle Anand; always ready to badger me with some teasing remark. But he wasn't about. The modest printing shop, which Sawmiss owned with his brother Satha, was open but deserted; it (like its owners) was having its customary afternoon nap. The grocer's on the opposite end of the corner was also open, deserted and dozing. But the autistic boy of the middle-aged Gujarati couple who owned the store was there as usual and, as usual, was scrambling about on the open stoep, covered in dust, rattling an assortment of roughly made wooden toys and gurgling a cacophony of half-human and half-animal sounds. I just didn't know what to think or what to feel when he saw him. I tried to pass by as quickly as I could, but the boy noticed me; halted, stopped his gurgling and looked at me point blank. I waited for a sign of recognition or acknowledgement but there was no response in the boy's bovine eyes. Then, as if no one was there, he went on playing and gurgling.

After the next house, the Hoxey's house, I came to the corner. Sixth Street was alive with the sound of play and talk. Small groups of girls stood together laughing, giggling and exchanging bits of conversation. Others were playing with a makeshift skipping rope. The boys, using a tennis ball, were playing football.

I had been a mediocre footballer before I entered hospital: all my Tamil-School friends played better than I did. Whenever there was a pick-'n'-play match about to be started I was always ignored and included only when there was no one else to pick; for no one was ever left out. So I made up my mind, once I left the hospital and started walking normally, to do everything possible to become a good footballer. I had this idea that everything could be self taught; so consequently I had gone into town on my own and bought myself a football manual.

It took me all of two days to read but I read every one of the seventy-six pages. I knew I had to have a ball; so I asked mother. It was an indulgence, but by then money had ceased to be a problem for the family: 226 had been completely renovated, the new kitchen had a new electric cooker and a new refrigerator, the bathroom had a new geyser and a new telephone-style shower, and there was, standing outside on the pavement, a new sky-blue Hudson car. Within days I was kicking around a new (made in Pakistan) leather ball.

I joined the street footballers by going up to Innie. "Hey, Innie can I fall in?"

"Ja, sure. They're one short on the other side. Play with them!"

"OK."

I turned to the other leading player, a tough and rough Dravidian-skinned waiter's son. "Hey Butcher, I'm playing with you. Innie says you're one short, OK?" Butcher's real name was Moonsamy, and he hated it — the quickest way to pick a fight with him was to go up to him and say: "How's it Moonsamy?"

"Ja, OK. I'm playing goalie and in. You can play goalie."

Playing goalie meant that Butcher didn't think I was any good as a player. I understood this but didn't mind so long as I could play.

The block-length stretch of Sixth Street, which fell under the shade of the Temple's red-brick wall and South Indian tower, was as dusty and as unkempt as the rest of the street. Traffic on it was scant; so the Tamil-School children used it as playground and as a home-made football pitch.

I saved a goal with my right foot.

I wanted to play in and enjoy the beautiful thrill of scoring a goal. The bell rang but the game, as if it had a will of its own, continued.

"Hey we'd better go!" Boya, my cousin, called. I hadn't noticed but half the players had already abandoned the game. Butcher, Innie and I gathered our books and slipped into the school. We crept past the walled flower beds that dotted the inside perimeter of the School and the Temple, ducked past the iron framed windows and then, like thieves in the night, entered the hall. The first half-hour was always a general assembly and the singing that always accompanied assembly had already begun. Then Saroj, one of the senior girls, read a passage from the Tamil version of the *Bhagavad Ghita*; but, since the text was in classical Tamil, to me she might as well have been reading in Hindi or Xhosa.

Assembly was almost over. Good, I thought, Khrishnaner hadn't spotted us. Khrishnaner, the main teacher, the principal and the head and brain of the school — his English was every bit as good as his Tamil — was formidable in more ways than one. I remembered the occasion when he slapped Butcher and left the imprint of his hand on Butcher's cheek a full minute.

I see this man now. He was, like my father, an unwavering teetotaler. He also had his daily shower as regular as sun rise but, unlike my father's, his — in winter as in summer — was cold.

I fixed my eyes on the man without whom nothing in the Tamil community could be done. He named, married, buried, drafted out wedding cards, wrote out epitaphs, read the stars and designed the Temple.

Now he stood there — his face like an amiable sphinx and his plain shirt and trousers like a just-rehabilitated hobo — and poised himself to close assembly. I looked at his leather shoes. I was embarrassed to see that their rear ends had been trod down and forced into the shape of rough slippers. It was such doings, I thought, which made the Indians seem, in the eyes of the Europeans, so backward. I looked critically at his baggy pants.

"You four, come here!" he ordered in a sergeant-like tone. He pointed to the front of the assembly with his withered but still menacing cane.

I despaired: "Oh, God, don't tell me he's going to cane us, here. Boy, how I hate these assemblies."

The four of us stood sheepishly in front of the grey wooden table, behind which Krishnaner (his hair beginning to show traces of grey) sat when he was teaching. He must have been in a mellow mood that afternoon; for the familiar and threatening: "Why are you late?" was not uttered. He ordered us to close ranks and then, using his cane, pointed to our shoes: "So you prefer football to punctuality and prayers?"

We all bowed our heads in affected guilt.

He addressed the assembly and, with his eyes fixed on us, reproached: "Look at the state of their shoes. You would think that big fellows like these ought to know better!"

This reference to big fellows was an exaggeration; for in the assembly that day there were bigger fellows still, fellows like Ranga and his contemporaries.

I looked furtively at my shoes. They were, indeed, in a sorry state: the laces were worn, stitches in more than one place were threatening to come loose, scratches and patches scarred and scuffed the toes and heels, and dust, red and thick, covered everything.

"You four, go out and get those shoes cleaned up immediately, and don't let me catch you coming in late with shoes looking like that again!"

Outside, disgraced, we used the row of taps that had been purposely installed for ablutions. We allowed the water to run freely over the top of our shoes; taking care not to wet our socks. The dust rolled away. I shook off the remaining water by kicking an imaginary football. The water affected a magic transformation: the shoes were now bright and shiny.

We re-entered the classroom, impatient to show Krishnaner our proud effort. I scrutinised his face, anxious to discover if it had registered a more indulgent and a less reproachful look, but was dismayed to see it snappishly disappointed, as if it was telling itself, "Brahma, Vishnu, Siva, what a bunch of clots I've got here!"

I looked down and was amazed to discover that the water during its evaporation had caked up the residue of dust on the uppers, had heightened the cracks and the patches, and had transformed bad into worse.

* * *

Another afternoon, probably a year later, I see myself leaving 226, turning left and, with deliberate slow steps, walking down Grand Street. I remember I had taken the resolution to mentally revise my homework while making my way to school.

And what was my homework? Write out a passage and learn it off by heart; this was the essential intellectual demand of a Tamil-School day. I didn't mind copying out a paragraph or two from a Tamil reader, even if it was written for far-away Tamils in far-away India. I recall now that the Tamil letters, more elaborate and more attractive than the white Roman letters, fascinated me — and they still do. But it was vexation to learn off lines by heart, whether it was about village India or not. Worse still was the punishment: the caning that followed if I wasn't able to recite the given passage; so year in and year out I submitted to the assigned drudge. What a waste of time. I remember telling myself that if I had a kid one day, I would never send him to Tamil School.

I avoided the parched, dusty pavements even though the tarred surface of the street was hot. I kept towards the edge of the left pavement and managed to stay, more or less, in the shade. I picked up, as I passed Lalie's Café, the smell of vienna sausages and chips. Dust whirled about. It was hot. I felt the heat penetrate the soles of my shoes.

The little concentration I had was dissipated when my eyes fell on the poster of *The Magnificent Obsession*. Rock Hudson and Jane Wyman made me yearn for Saturday. My thoughts shifted to Jane Wyman and to the film, *Johnny Belinda*. Will I ever see it? I remember hearing grownups saying that the film was banned for under eighteens because someone rapes Jane Wyman.

I came to the corner of Grand and Fifth Streets and I clearly heard the voices of Doris Day and Gordon MacRae:

Tea for two,
And you for me.
Nobody to see us ...

Farther down the street, at Tip Top Printers, the lyrics and the music of the song were drowned out by the whirring of the print machines. I looked up at the first floor window. Sometimes Dickie Moodley was there. It had become a sort of custom to exchange greetings and snatches of conversation, but this time he wasn't there. Dickie (he was really Ranga's contemporary) was a sloppy Joe. He couldn't care two hoots for the way he dressed but he was a great footballer; he was also funny and, with his Burt-Lancaster smile, handsome.

I reached Sixth Street just in time to hear the bell ringing.

Tammy on that particular day was uneventful. I received no punishment, mainly because Khrishnaner's younger brother, Fisher, who was deputising (Khrishnaner was occupied with some Europeans who wanted to visit the Temple) forgot to demand the usual recitation chore.

At five o'clock Tamil School, thankfully, came to an end. I gathered my reader and my notebook and impatiently followed some others who were as anxious as I was to leave the Temple grounds. When we reached the little exit gate, we found that it had been locked.

I heard someone curse: "Oh, God man, it's Friday today — we've got to bloody well pray!"

It was still warm, though dusk was setting in, but the thought of taking off my shoes and socks, and washing my feet under cold water irritated me. But there was no choice. Fisher was already ordering those of us who had assembled on the Temple stoep into three strict graduated lines. Dahly, a good-natured widow, with a penchant for brandy, was lining up the girls in similar fashion. The boys and girls now faced each other across a makeshift aisle.

Fisher placed me at the edge of the last row. This gave me

61

a clear view of the girls. Dannaw, placed at the edge of the third row, was squarely in front of me. We all said she had lovely rounded breasts. Innie even boasted that one day he had brushed past her and he swore that they were genuine: "Nah, that cherrie doesn't need falsies."

The fragrance of incense and camphor, the aroma of bananas and coconut, and the cool scent of clay emanating from the freshly swept brick floor made me feel curiously insignificant and surprisingly pious. I didn't know why this was so or what incident produced it or what event caused it but I sensed (though the sensation was neither neat nor precise) that there was something two-faced and grovelling about prayers. My eyes discreetly explored Dannaw's anatomy. I discovered she had superbly shaped hands and feet. I adored the sweet delicateness of the female hand and the enigmatic charm of the exposed female feet. But prayers began. I closed my eyes, *sammied* with my hands and mechanically sang the familiar but incomprehensible Tamil prayer songs.

A family, the Govenders, were present. They were making an prayer offering; so food was going to be distributed. After downing a refreshing glass of sweet lemon water, I left the Temple and the school with my mini parcel of food in a little brown paper bag, which, by this time, was well-smudged with grease. Outside I opened the bag and peered in: *saccra sadoor, pouli sadoor*, some *caadlair*, half a banana and quarter of an orange. I tackled the sour rice first and then the sweet rice when all of a sudden I heard an ear-shattering bang. Butcher, as rough and tough as ever, already finished, had inflated his empty bag and smashed it between the palms of his hand.

11

On another Friday, no Govenders, Pillays, Naidoos, Padyachys, Chettys, Kolapens or Moodleys were present. Boya told Innie, Butcher and I that he knew of a sure-fire way of dodging prayers. The school and the Temple were self-contained, fortified. The west side was blocked off by a ten-feet-high wall; the north side by the hall which served as a school and as a venue for weddings and public meetings; the south side by a wall and an adjoining house; and the east side by a wall again and by two gates of contrasting size: the large one, made of wood and in line with the base of the tower, was the main (wedding-day) entrance; and the small one, made of metal, was the everyday entrance. The small gate was generally unlocked because it facilitated the entry of one and all to both the Temple and the school but Khrishnaner had it locked on Fridays; so the others and I wondered what Boya had in mind.

Yet his plan turned out to be straightforward. He wanted us to escape by scaling the west wall, which was on the blind side of the prayer stoep. He explained the strategy in a whisper: "We wash our feet last at this tap" — there was a single tap next to the corner of the wall. "We'll deliberately take our time and wait for prayers to start. Once the singing starts you get up here." He pointed to the top of the tap and to the bit of piping jutting out of the wall. Yes, it was evident, it did make a handy platform. "From here you have to jump to reach and to grip the top of the wall. Then you pull yourself up, see if the coast is clear and then you let yourself down on the other side and then jump — but you must go over barefoot: if someone should come before you're over, you can always come down again, drop your shoes and make

63

out that you were on your way to prayers. OK? Now, I'll show you how it's done."

He smiled and winked and went over before anyone could say Jack Robinson. I followed with less speed and less agility. Outside I found that Boya had crossed Fifth Street and was waiting for me on the Royal's stoep. I darted across, cleared the high embankment and joined him. A few seconds later Butcher and then Innie joined us. I felt elated and free and the twinkling eyes of my companions indicated that I wasn't the only one. We three POPs (prisoners of prayers) nudged each other and burst out into a gleeful laugh. We spent a minute looking at the photographic posters of the week's showing: Audie Murphy in *To Hell and Back*.

"Let's see what's showing next week," Innie suggested. We entered the foyer. *The Silver Chalice*! Boya called out. "Who's the lightee?" Innie inquired. I was still thinking of Audie Murphy as a cowboy in *Destry* and was wondering how he would be in a war film when Boya said, "Some guy called Paul New ... Man — Paul Newman."

"Who?" Butcher asked.

Not wanting to repeat the name Boya, pressing his finger against the glass, indicated that Butcher could read for himself. I sensed that the others, like myself, were disappointed that it wasn't someone we knew, someone like Victor Mature or Tyrone Power.

* * *

Thereafter, I remember we agreed that we would dodge Friday prayers once every fortnight. Our second effort went off as smoothly as the first. On our third attempt Boya had climbed the wall and was momentarily perched on the ledge, readying himself to roll over and to jump — my foot was on the tap ready to follow suit. I watched his movement and secretly admired his agility when a familiar voice of authority, short-circuited his action: "If you put half the effort you put into your escaping prayers, God might forgive you. C'mon jump!"

Boya just had time for a panicky whisper: "Arra! Khrishnaner!"

Butcher, Innie and myself, feigning complete innocence, quickly joined the prayer meeting.

After what seemed like an hour or so, I spied my cousin being led by the ear into the classroom. It was pathetic. Anxiety besieged me: was my cousin going to spill the beans? Sometimes, I didn't know if I liked Boya or not. I told myself, "He is after all a blood relation — his father is my mother's brother — and he certainly is generous: when he has sweets, he always calls me from across the street and shares them with me, but he has this bloody habit of boasting and lying."

I recalled a summer afternoon. Boya and I were sitting on the ground with our backs resting against the half-walled fence of 226 and spitting between our legs to see whose spit would resist evaporation the longest when Satchoo, from Cowie Street, came up. He joined us but turned down our invitation to spit. I could see by the way he was mootching that he wanted to tell us something.

"Hey, what's up Satch?"

"Naw, yesterday a white man came to our house," he glowed. "My mother made him some badja and tea, and he drank and ate with my father — have you guys had a white man to your place?" he asked, as if he was sure that we hadn't.

I knew that some white salesmen, now and then, stopped at Abdul Supplies Store. They came either from the Pretoria Tobacco Company or from some wholesale sweet company, offering either new cigarette brands or new sweet lines. I expected Boya to mention them but I knew for certain that they were never invited into the purely utilitarian house that lay quietly and unnoticed behind the shop, and I also knew that they never solicited such invitations. Cousin was obviously waiting for me to say something first.

"Oh, there's a white couple who often come to our place." I tried to sound matter-of-fact. "Mr and Mrs Parker. Actually he's an Englishman and she's a Boer."

The Parkers were farmers who preferred to sell their fruit, their peaches, apricots and plums, direct to my father. Mr Parker, who curiously resembled the British actor Cecil Parker, was genteel and placid. Mrs Parker, younger than her

65

husband, was forthright with a commanding voice and a commanding choice of words that matched her large bones and her tough face, but her bossiness was tempered by a ready and bubbling cordiality.

As the first white woman I had encountered, she impressed me and as the first independent woman I saw, she intrigued me. She always sought out mother in the kitchen or at the back of the house, where she would address her with a species of pro-feminist badgering: "C'mon Mrs Naidoo, come and join us in the sitting room!" When the Parkers came, it was the habit of my mother to serve tea and to leave them in the company of my father. She always bashfully refused Mrs Parker's invitation with a smile that seemed to say: "You are mischievous, Mrs Parker, you know perfectly well that Indian women never behave like that."

My cousin, starting with the salesmen, invented a score of white visitors and invented, above all, extremely cosy tea sessions. He lied like a conjurer. Satchoo looked at me and said, "Nee man, hy lig." I smiled and said, "Of course, he is." Then Boya, taking me quite unawares, said, as if butter couldn't melt in his mouth: "No, I'm not lying. Satya Maa."

I was outraged. Not so much by his blatant lies as by the sacrilege of his oath.

"Hey, stop your shit! You know you're lying. Why bring your mother into this thing?"

"Hey, you leave my mother alone! You leave her out of this!" And, after a fraction of a pause, Boya roughly added: "The Parkers' ass!"

"Hey, watch it, cousin!"

"Don't bloody cousin me!"

I could barely refrain from clouting him one. But, anticipating my anger and my intended action, he darted across the street and gained the stoep and the safety of Abdul Supplies Store, his father's shop. From this haven he became more provocative and more brazen: he stuck his tongue out and pulled faces at me.

"I'll get you!" I threatened.

"You won't get me nothing, you assy Parker!"

"I'm going to tell my mother you swore the Parkers."

"Voetsek! Anyway your mother does this!"

In a standing position, he crudely simulated the act of fornication. At such moments, beside myself with rage, I was quite prepared to strangle him. Yet somehow we always let bygones be bygones. Still, Boya was unpredictable and, sometimes, downright callous: on one occasion, just for the fun of it, he dumped a new-born kitten down their toilet and pulled the chain.

Now I wondered if he was going to turn stool pigeon. I knew he wasn't one to collaborate, but would his loyalty stand up to the threat of pain and punishment. Krishnaner joined the prayer meeting. I did not dare to open my eyes: my instinct told me that his eyes at that very moment were sweeping across our faces like a searchlight. The prayers came to an end. There was no detention. Cousin came good.

* * *

Whenever there was a Tamil death, the bereaved family immediately contacted Khrishnaner. His counsel and presence were indispensable. If the death occurred just before two o'clock in the afternoon, it meant that Tamil School for that day would be cancelled. Khrishnaner was absent sometimes when a vital meeting had to be attended, sometimes when an important ceremony, not connected to death, had to be performed. These occurrences, however, were rare. Death and funerals remained the prime negators of Tammy.

I was well aware of this and was therefore surprised when my brother Ranga one afternoon said he knew of a sure way to get school cancelled.

"How?" I asked him. My brother waved aside my query with a wait-and-see response. I persisted. He gave in and said, "By prayer."

"Prayer?" He must be joking, I told myself.

I knew that Ranga was orthodox when it came to religion and I was aware that he expressed no misgivings or doubts about the ceremonies, the customs, the convictions and all the other paraphernalia of our religious humdrum. I found even at that early age that the goings-on of my elders, especially those of my mother and aunties, were whimsical and alien and remote from the concerns of the Location. I already harboured a half-formed desire to contest the panoply of rituals and beliefs, but unsure and quite unable to expose their irrelevancies and irrationalities, I desisted. But no Tammy seemed worth a prayer. There was, anyway, nothing to lose.

I pondered over the problem of how we were going to get into the recess of the Temple, where prayers were customarily held, without being spotted by the other pupils; for if they saw us they would surely think we had gone clean off our rockers. No school-child, certainly no boy, ever went voluntarily to pray. Prayers were the prerogative of grown-ups, and mostly women at that. I was just about to ask Ranga how we were going to solve this particular problem when all at once I realized we were moving away from the Tamil School.

"Where are we going to pray?"

"The Vulca at home!"

I pictured the ornamental oil lamp with Ganes embossed on it; saw my mother reverentially cleaning it; saw it in its hand-made hardboard altar; and felt its aura of pomp and power.

Appealing to God at home? Wouldn't God, I wanted to ask Ranga, be more generous and more open to appeal in the Temple. I held my tongue as faith in his enterprise began to falter and yet I wanted to believe. I comforted myself: God always, sooner or later, answers prayers. Then I wondered how would God, supposing he did hear our prayers, intervene? Would somebody die, and who? The implications of our prayer suddenly dawned on me, but I reassured myself: *surely God wouldn't do anything as rash as that.* He'll arrange a meeting or something but surely not a death.

Yet it was already past one o'clock, time was running out. It was impossible for a meeting at this late hour to take place. Logically the only way Tammy could be cancelled was by death. I ceased to think. I told myself, we are going to pray to God, we are going to think about the cancellation of Tammy and the rest was up to Him.

It was Wednesday; 226 was deserted. Our mother had gone to the Orient cinema to see one of those Indian melodramas

68

where song and dance and no kissing went hand in hand with flying monkeys, triple-headed demons and miracles galore. The Vulca was tucked away in an obscure corner of the little used and spotlessly clean dining-room. It was possible to pray there in the afternoons without courting attention.

We readied ourselves. Ranga instructed me: be sincere in wishing for the cancellation and keep your eyes closed until the prayers are completely over. I listened and obeyed. Ranga led with the chanting, a low bass voice and I, with my high octave, followed. After a minute or so the first prayer was over. I kept my eyes shut and waited, wondering which of the many other prayer-songs would follow. Silence — long seconds of silence — until: "Hey, what are you doing?"

I opened my eyes and quickly queried, "Is it finished?" Ranga nodded, while eyeing me with an of-course-it's-finished look and then, using the movement of his head again, he indicated that we had to leave. Once outside I told him that I was baffled to find that he considered only one prayer sufficient to do the trick.

"Last week, on Wednesday, was there school?" The unexpected question flustered me.

"No, but ..."

"Well, I prayed the same prayer and it worked." I didn't say anything. I tried to recollect the details of the previous week's cancellation. "Hey, there was a death. Koffieluisbard, the old Tamil School teacher died!" That is what I wanted to tell him but I checked myself, just in time. A disquiet set in. I suddenly felt a pang of conscience. But once again I pushed it away, shook off the remaining doubt, forgot the unease and followed my brother, in a quiet confident stroll back to school.

Sixth Street outside the Temple was deserted. Faith in God and the efficacy of prayer bubbled and glowed within me. I couldn't wait to hear from one of our colleagues. The pounding in my breast quickened. I ached with the longing to hear the magic words, "no Tammy today." As our feet carried us closer to the School, my ears picked up the familiar sounds of the very prayer we had just offered to Ganes at 226 — assembly had already started.

69

* * *

Jesse James gets on to a chair and is about to hang up a framed picture. One of his men, turned traitor, creeps up from behind with a colt in his hand.

Jesse James (with Tyrone Power and Henry Fonda), one of the Location's favourite films, had (and still has) special significance for me. When the Royal first showed it, I wasn't born; when it re-showed it, I was still a toddler and when it showed it again, I decided, since I wasn't allowed to go to the cinema at night, that I wouldn't miss it even if it meant dodging Tammy.

Royal cinema on that fateful summer afternoon was packed. The unmistakable odour of dagga (akin to the burning of tea leaves), wafting in from the front seats, was particularly powerful and pungent that day. But once the film started I forgot the smoky vapour, the oppressive fumes, the smell of tobacco, ganja and sweat — I forgot even the noise of peanut shells cracking under shuffling feet and the itchy discomfort of the worn out seats. Hollywood celluloid unwound and began to cast its spell. But my peace and bliss was interrupted by the torch light of Fixit, the usher boy, just at the moment when Jesse James was about to be betrayed and killed. Why was he singling me out? The sound of Ambi's voice, coming from behind the glare of the lamp in a whisper, made me gulp: "Jay, Hamma knows you didn't go to school. Khrishnaner sent somebody home to ask for you. Hamma says she's going to tell Papa when he comes. You'd better come home!"

My mother had kept Ambi and Ruby home that day because the dressmaker wanted to see them that afternoon for a fitting. Ambi — I found out later — had acted on her own: she had hurried to the cinema as soon as Khrishnaner's errand-boy had left. Once outside, the additional information completed the disaster of my truancy. I expected nothing good. I resigned myself to the inevitable.

At home my mother, angry and shocked, gave me short shrift: "Go to your room and wait!"

70

It was an eternity before I heard the familiar rattle of the truck, which my father had bought secondhand, pull up on to the pavement and then switch off. Then I heard my mother lodging her complaint and asking her husband to correct his son. Father, a man of few words, made no comment but simply asked: "Where's he?" I now heard his soft measured footsteps approach the room but before they reached it, they turned and went to the back of the yard where the coal and the empty fruit boxes were stored. I strained to pick out the sounds of his movements. I heard a box break. My heart sank: I was in for a hiding. Involuntary tears crowded my eyes. Why should my father and I come to this pass.

The door opened and through the cloudiness of moist eyes I saw my father's face, handsome, inquiring and stern, and yet betraying an almost imperceptible sign of — was it amusement? But a glance at his right hand quickly dispelled that idea; for there like a curse come true was a strip of the long dark wood that made up the sides of the large beetroot and carrot crates. Tears, which all the while were welling up, burst their confines and cascaded silently over my flushed cheeks. I made no move, no sound.

"Your mother says you didn't go to Tamil School today and that you were sitting in the bioscope! Is that true?"

The voice and the question brooked no nonsense. It was hopeless to explain or to deny. I nodded, half in trepidation, half in shame. A brief but seemingly long moment of silence ensued. My tears became autonomous. He hesitated. I vainly tried to read his thoughts. Time stood still. I saw the hand holding the plank — the hand of a chef and not a butcher — relax. Finally he broke the heavy silence with: "Well, don't let me catch you again!" Shamefaced, I nodded. My father turned round and left the room. Less than a year later, without permission and without notification, I left Tamil School, for good and all.

12

A photo of an old Swaraj team hung on one of the walls of my parents' bedroom. I often stood in front of it, scrutinised it and wondered about the people I saw there: shopkeepers, hawkers, waiters, teachers, drunks and my father. Did these people really in their youth play football? Could age really effect such dramatic and radical changes? The transition between youth and mature adulthood was a riddle wrapped in a mystery. I just couldn't picture them doing what I did on the football ground, but the photo, silent and singular, and the testimony of my mother, simple and straightforward, were there; and yet my disbelief wouldn't be chivvied, not entirely.

Swaraj, in some uncanny way, seemed to be inseparably linked with the Tamil community, with the Temple, with my uncles and with Khrishnaner. Rajendran, Khrishnaner's son, played for Swaraj. He was one of the stars of the team, one of the select group of players in that magnificent eleven which beat the great Johannesburg side, Moonlight Rangers, in a Transvaal District cup final. To my childhood mind that Swaraj team was as magic as Real Madrid and Honved. But Rajendran died within a year in a tragic drowning accident. Shortly thereafter seven other players, because of a row with officials, quit the club.

These seven players, which included the goalkeeper, were all highly talented. Five were very good and two, Issie and Bagas, were exceptional. Issie was a small, wizardly player; Bagas had speed, a good dribble and an explosive left foot. But, with the loss of Rajendran and the withdrawal of the seven players, Swaraj — overnight — became a phantom team. Only Dickie Moodley of the three remaining players was exceptional. He was then just eighteen, yet on his shoulders fell the burden of building up a new Swaraj side. He managed, by fielding eleven players, to keep the team alive, but the name, and the red, white, and green colours were the only things that the new team had in common with the old.

I remember even now the sour atmosphere and the feeling of betrayal that hung over the football community when the ex-Swaraj players not only left Swaraj but also the Pretoria District Football Association. They formed a new team, Farouk Rangers, and they joined the rival Pretoria Muslim District Football Association. The secular football association had a ground right next to the non-secular association, but Pretoria's Muslim community was far too small to field a real league: Sunday after Sunday Iqbal Rangers played Farouk Rangers or Farouk Rangers played Iqbal Rangers — the Muslim Association was a farce. After a fruitless year Farouk Rangers came to its senses, changed its name to plain Rangers and returned to the fold of the Pretoria District Football Association.

* * *

As was to be expected Rangers had it in for Swaraj and Swaraj (whatever there was left of it) had it in for Rangers. Two years after the depletion of the Swaraj side, the two teams met for the first time one Sunday afternoon.

In previous matches Rangers had already shown what they could do. They had roundly beaten Pretorians, Cambridge, Stellas and Pirates; Swaraj, against the same teams, had, just as roundly, lost all its matches. Nobody, except the Swaraj players and the Swaraj officials, thought Swaraj stood a chance against Rangers.

The Wednesday afternoon just before the vital Sunday, some of the Arsenal players (Arsenal was a junior team that played exclusively on Sunday mornings) and some of the Swaraj players were busy practising at opposite ends of the field. Dickie Moodley spotted me among the Arsenal players and made his way, in a trot, towards me.

"Hey Jay, how about playing goalie for us on Sunday?"

73

"Hey Dickie, you're joking. You know I'm not ready!"

"Look we don't have a goalie. This is our number one problem for Sunday's match. You know, I think we got a side that can give those bastards a real go, give them a good run for their money but we've got to have a goalkeeper."

I thought of expressing unwillingness in some other way but I could see my words weren't going to have any effect.

"Look we don't have a goalie. We tried Commaras. He's all right as a full back, but as a goalie he's lousy. We tried Raymond; OK as a full back but hopeless as a goalie. No, you know you're better than any one of them, any day."

Dickie saw my reticence; so he added: "I've asked Veegee to sign on. We've got him in the side for Sunday."

I knew Veegee was good and I also knew he was a year younger than I was. Yes, I thought, Veegee might just make it but he's in the forward line whereas I'll be in the defence and I'll have to cope with the tricks of Issie and the left foot of Bagas. It wasn't the same thing. But the distinction I saw so bright and clear would appear, in Dickie's eyes, as mere hair splitting; so I resigned myself to repeating: "No Dickie, I feel I'm not ready. I'm not saying this because I want you to beg me. You know, I'm not like that. I'm scared of mucking it up and letting you and the other guys down." Imagine, I told myself, if they lose the match because of me. "Besides, Dickie, I'm not sixteen yet. The regulations say we can only sign on once we're sixteen."

"Ah, that's not a problem. I told you, Veegee signed and he's going to play."

"Nah, I'm sorry Dickie, I know I'm not ready yet!"

I turned and walked away. I heard no more of the affair and I was glad.

On the following Sunday I was in my room at the back of the house reading an article in *The Football Monthly* about the Welsh international, John Charles — the Gentle Giant, my favourite player — when Ruby entered my room and said: "Jay, Papa wants to see you. He's on the stoep."

It was still early in the morning; for Sunday was the day father cooked boiled or European food in the new kitchen and it was his habit to start about ten a.m. Before that he sat

74

or stood outside on the stoep contemplating the passing world or inspecting the garden. When I reached the stoep, I immediately understood what was up. There was a delegation of four Swaraj players — Dickie, was one of them. It was obvious they had been there a little while.

"Jay, these fellows got an important match today. They want you to help them out. They think you can do it. What do you say?"

I knew I couldn't give a negative answer, not in front of my father. I knew I was cornered. I knew I had to say yes. "Ja, OK," I said, trying my best not to reveal my irritation.

* * *

Rain clouds gathered; it was unusual, but winter proper had not yet set in. A few drops fell on the dry hard surface and released the refreshing and friendly scent of wet grass.

The two teams, in striped jerseys — Rangers in black and white with black collars (I think they should have been called Pirates); Swaraj in red and white with green collars — positioned themselves for the kick off. The crowd was large, larger than the average Sunday crowd. The sky remained grey and overcast. The whistle blew.

Play, for the first five minutes, looked promising. Swaraj, thanks to the tireless efforts of Dickie, dominated the midfield. Veegee, once or twice, broke through the Rangers defence. A murmur rose among the crowd and a mysterious sensation gripped them and told them that Swaraj could pull it off. The show-off arrogance of the Rangers' players, especially the seven ex-Swaraj ones, wilted. I jumped up and down on my goal line. I had just seen Berea Park play; so I imagined myself to be Aubrey Tirrell. Somebody gave me a chewing gum just before I got on to the field. My jaws worked away. I moved to the right and touched the goal post and repeated the action on the left. My eyes all the while remained fixed on the ball. Maybe, I thought, this will be my day, after all. I saw myself pulling off one or two dramatic and spectacular saves, and I gloried in the status that I anticipated would attend me at school the following day.

Dickie from the twenty-five yard line accelerated and shifted into one of his buccaneer runs. He swerved past one player, feinted and swept past another and, a fraction later, his right foot cocked, triggered and fired. The ball blasted off and careered slightly outward. The Rangers goalkeeper was too advanced. The crowd, on the Swaraj side, cried "goal!" The goalkeeper stretched his neck backwards to follow the flight of the ball and then, to his relief, he saw it crash against the crossbar. From my end, I heard the disappointing thud. The ball bounced back into play and was booted out for a throw in.

But this Swaraj pressure was ephemeral: Issie and Bagas camped in the Swaraj half. I saw Bagas's left foot snap and followed the ball which, like a sky rocket, went whistling over the crossbar. Then Issie sent an easy one straight towards me. I took the ball safely with both hands and, to make sure, covered it with my chest. The ball felt unusually hard and heavy, the lacing already rough and abrasive. I was flattered that Issie and Bagas, the two seigneurs of the Location, were honouring me in this way. I felt important and almost big. My gut sensations dizzily darted across the borders of boyhood and youth.

Rangers's attacks increased. Issie spotted an opening and lobbed a pass over Dickie's head to Aggie, his younger brother. Aggie dropped the ball, caught the Swaraj right back on the wrong foot, swept past the penalty spot and closed in towards me. I cursed and advanced. An instruction picture from my football manual flashed in my mind. My body obeyed: I closed the angle of the goal. I screwed up my courage and prepared to do a dare-devil dive at the feet of the oncoming player. I was comforted by the fact that Aggie was more a matador than a bull. But in the momentum of his break, he easily swerved past me and with spry elegance chivvied the ball towards the unprotected goal. As helpless as an infant fallen from a cot, I looked on as the ball entered the net.

Five minutes later Bagas lobbed a pass to Issie. Issie tied the ball to his feet, slipped past a defender and entered the penalty area. Once again, marooned, I came out still hopeful.

I sensed that Issie was going for the right side of the goal. I covered my left. But Issie had been simulating: he smartly chipped the ball to the left and left me floundering on the wrong foot. The sad task of collecting the ball from the back of the goal was performed a second, third and fourth time. Then the whistle blew: half time.

During the pause officials and stubborn fans rallied to the players. But I looked on in silence. I realized that the Swaraj defence could not cope with an attack which had, after all, destroyed the famous Moonlighter's defence. But I hoped that the damage could be limited: a four-nil defeat, I thought, would be clear humiliation but acceptable.

The match resumed and it was evident that the panache in the Rangers attack had ceased. I began to hope again.

Twenty minutes from the end a light but steady rain came down. The ground grew swollen and became heavy. A greyish haze enveloped the field. The burden of defence on Dickie's shoulders began to tell; he could manage the job of two players but not of three. A crack appeared in the Swaraj defence and after the rain the crack became a fissure: Bagas scored — five nil; Issie scored again — six nil; Hassan scored — seven nil; Aggie scored a third time — eight nil; Bagas scored again — nine nil.

Five minutes from the end Bagas offered one of his specials. The shot, from just outside the eighteen-yard area, came in like a cannon ball. I saw it coming before it came. I positioned myself and with a backward leap, twisting and sailing through the air like Nijinski, I pushed it over the crossbar. Applause from all sides broke out from the spectator lines.

Minutes before the final whistle, Issie broke past the defence with one of his close, crisp dribbles. Again I had to confront a goal-scorer on my own. I advanced, dived at Issie's feet but I was neatly side-stepped. Issie moved towards the goal line, stopped the ball, got down on his knees and, bending over (as if he was facing Mecca) pushed the ball across the line with his head — ten nil.

13

I knew already when I was about six years old that adults had sex. At that time Savitri, a neighbour who was my age, agreed to play mother and father with me. We slipped into the bathroom of 226 without being noticed by anybody. We took some of the clothes from the washing basket, spread it out on the green-polished cement floor, undressed from the waist downward and tried to have sex. My penis touched her vagina and we convinced ourselves that we had accomplished our mother-father thing.

When I got interested in football I practically put sex aside; so when I came out of hospital I had no idea that there was such a thing as masturbation. It was Innie who provided the enlightenment.

"What, you haven't skommelled yet? You must be joking man! Hey, you don't know how to do this?" He dropped his hand between his legs and moved them like a dice player before throwing.

"I do it when I'm having a bath. The next time you have a bath, you know, the skin on your kungie, it can go up and down; well you take it in your hand like this." — he clasped his hand as if he was holding a torch — "and you shake. Let the skin come forward and backwards. You'll see your laat get stiff and hard. Well, just keep going and then you'll see a white liquid squirting out and then you'll thank heaven for messy things."

I wasn't sure if he was having me on or not. But I did as he instructed and found that he was no liar.

One late evening when we were sitting on the ledge of Auntie Jaytoon's veranda wall (at the corner of Grand and Sixth Streets), Innie suddenly said: "Hey, you've got to have

78

a cherrie. You're the only one amongst us who hasn't got a bokkie. Veegee and I have found someone for you — a really nice girl, with lekker legs."

I looked at Innie, waiting for him to mention a name or to give me some indication of just who he had in mind. I turned to Veegee but his boyish and slightly wayward grin gave nothing away. In the meanwhile Innie simulated the sound of a clarinet and the action of a clarinet player. What is he up to? I asked myself.

"Do you know Soobathie, Dieya's daughter?" Innie teasingly asked. Yes, Dieya, he played the clarinet for the Barathia Orchestra, a Tamil band, the group that provided the dreary Indian music at Tamil weddings. Yes, Soobathie. I knew exactly who they had in mind: a quiet and attractive girl who was shorter than myself — I couldn't bear the thought of having a girl taller, heavier or larger than myself; yes, she had nice legs and a bashful smile. I didn't think much of Dieya but I wasn't going to go out with him. I liked the idea but I pretended indifference.

"Ja, she's not bad."

"So, is it OK?" Innie got excited. "Look, give us the go-ahead and tomorrow Quenma, you know, Veegee's cherrie — they're always together — will talk you right. I'll bet that Soobathie will never say no."

"OK," I said.

Innie tapped me on the back. "That's the bloody spirit, man."

Two days later I received a reply. It was, as Innie had predicted, positive. I was going to have my first date. Now came the difficult part: where could we meet? I thought of the School's grounds where lovers sometimes met at night. But what happened if we should get caught and chased away like thieves by Klaas or Andries, the School's caretakers? Or what happened if our out of bounds presence should be reported to Mr Caulineck? No, the prospect disheartened me.

I thought of the football ground. But it was remote and at night hazardous. Besides, there was that benumbing rumour that a "Coloured" couple had been caught there by a band of Africans (or were they "Coloureds"?): the man was badly beaten up and the woman was gang-raped. No, I was certainly not going to risk that. I finally decided, on the advice of Veegee, to meet my date next to the dairy near the abandoned sand football ground, which was now partly transformed into a Putco bus depot.

It was late autumn. The night was clear and bright and the still warm air was tempered by a slight breeze. It was still early, just after seven, but everybody was already indoors. Earlier I had taken a shower; now I put on my Levis blue jeans, a white tee shirt, a fawn buttoned-down shirt, a navy blue cardigan and a pair of black Jarman moccasins. I strolled down to the corner of Jerusalem and Boom Streets, turned left and went past Jeevan's Outfitters. I looked at my Rotary watch; it was 7.15 p.m. The date was fixed for 7.30.

Jeevan's imported a lot of American clothes. Their windows displayed outstanding American shirts and socks but I didn't stop to look. I went past the dry cleaners, Calliyan's Outfitters and Mooloo's Cafe. At Kalla's Cycle Store the loudspeakers outside were blaring out the sounds of Fat Domino's 'Blueberry Hill'. The music and the words entered my brain and set me off singing to myself:

I found my thrill
On Blueberry hill.
On Blueberry hill
Where I found you.
The moon stood still
On Blueberry hill.
It lingered until
My dreams came true.

I crossed the street and passed, once again, a row of outfitters' shops. I turned the corner and suddenly noticed that the soft grey sky line had darkened and night had fallen. I could just make out the all-in-one dairy and fishery, and the printing shop next door. I had to strain my eyes before I discerned two shadows up against the wire fence that adjoined the printing shop. I got closer and could see it was Quenma and Soobathie.

I felt a sudden stirring of my pulse. I looked up at the sky, it was full of stars all looking, as if they were just waiting to see how I was going to perform. A glance behind confirmed that the street was empty. The general silence was intermittently cut by the buzz of a vehicle racing up or down Boom Street. Quenma came towards me. She looked at me and said, her face lit up with collaboration, "I'll be just around the corner, OK." I smiled and nodded.

Soobathie was leaning against the fence. I could see that she was still wearing her navy-blue school uniform. As I narrowed the distance between us, all sensation in my feet evaporated. It was, as if they had suddenly disappeared. I stopped and, seized by panic, inspected the ground. I was relieved to find that they were still there. Sensation just as mysteriously seeped back into them. Soobathie must have thought I had trodden on something and that I had stopped to see what it was. She looked happy and excited. Her fresh complexion, under the shadowy light of the night, was bright and warm. My body, upon seeing her welcoming smile, relaxed but the muscles on my jaw twitched once or twice.

"Hello!" I didn't recognize my voice.

"Hello!" Hers sounded cosy and reassuring.

Silence.

I looked into her eyes and at her lips and then reached quietly and cautiously for her hand. She touched my arm and, with the other hand, played with a button on my cardigan. I wondered how Patrick in my place would have behaved. He'd ask her for a kiss. Yes, that's it, I'll ask her for a kiss — that'll break the ice.

"Can I — may I kiss you?"

She smiled and demurely nodded assent. I bent forward, a wisp of her hair brushed softly past my temple. A warm tremor ran through my body. I sensed the joy and fragrance of her body and the pristine promise of flesh: soft, inviting, mysterious. I closed my eyes, pursed my lips and plunged. Our lips touched, my thoughts and intelligence blacked out. A soft delicious vibration skipped and jumped through my flesh and blood. I opened my eyes and drew back.

I wasn't sure if I was waking from a dream or if I was really

81

doing what I had done. I suddenly felt a desperate need to be away, to be alone, to pinch myself and to convince myself that I had really done what I did — that my kiss was deed and not dream, that I had received the gift of flesh and desire, that I was, indeed, awake.

"Well, I can't stay too long, I must go now. I'll see you again."

I didn't stop to see if she was surprised or not. I went across the barren field towards ABC Bakery and from there circled round and joined Jerusalem Street by passing through Mogul Street. As soon as I was out of sight, I threw my head back and, looking at the stars as if they were intimate friends, took a deep breath and then set off on a free and easy sprint.

14

Mr Pather often came to 226. I didn't quite understand why he came to the Location. My mother told me, in a vague sort of way, that it was business that brought him to Pretoria. I knew we had relatives in Durban, in the Clairwood area, but Mr Pather, I was certain, was no relative. I asked Ranga about it one day and he explained that the Location didn't have a hotel and our house was one of the few places where, without much inconvenience, he could be put up.

I see him now. A thin man of medium height, he wore stiff attached collars and cuffs, blue striped shirts, soft-coloured tailor-made suits and plain but immaculate shoes. There was something that gave him an unaffected gentlemanly air: his speech, the way he held his newspaper, the fact that he had a toilet bag and wore brass arm-bands — something definitely made him different from and superior to the other men of the Location.

After I left the hospital I went to stay with the Pathers to recuperate.

When I got to Durban, I found that they lived in a very large house. I was surprised to learn that the house had belonged to whites and I was even more surprised to discover that their neighbours, on each side, were white as well. Impressively, the house had an indoor and an outdoor toilet. The Pathers referred to the one outside as the servants' toilet. I was under the impression that 226 was a comfortable house because over at Scotland Yard, at the corner of Grand and Sixth Streets, at least ten families shared a single Turkish toilet and a bathroom with neither a bath nor a shower. Similar yards, nearby, had similar convenience facilities, but compared to the Pather house even 226 seemed a little primitive. I was also struck by the spaciousness of the house: there was a large garden in front and a larger one at the back, and in the latter garden there was a giant mango tree top-heavy with ripening fruit.

Mrs Pather, a handsome but stoic woman, treated me with reserve; Mr Pather treated me with favour. He spoke to me, as if he wanted to improve my understanding of the world, as if, in some uncanny way, he understood that Jopa was no longer about. He drove me to the port in his old Studebaker car; he showed me a gym where an experienced white boxer was sparring with an inexperienced black one; he talked knowingly of Durban; he carefully pointed out what editorials in newspapers were; he stressed their importance and encouraged me to make a habit of reading them.

I kept my eyes and ears wide open that day. I could sense and discern that black and white in Durban weren't as rigidly separated as they were in Pretoria. I saw black and white using the same buses. I felt the curious absence of Afrikaans. I also saw something I had never seen in Pretoria: Indian petrol attendants, Indian refuse collectors, Indian street sweepers — Indians, in sum, doing all the menial tasks which in Pretoria were reserved for Africans. This puzzled me but I thought it would be inappropriate to ask Mr Pather about it. I also saw something that would have been inconceivable in Pretoria: a white man, tall and powerful, in full view of everyone, shamelessly thrash a scrawny-looking Indian. The Indian seemed to be a flower seller and the white man a passerby. I found the passivity of the Indian hard to understand. Why didn't he resist or run away? Mr Pather didn't stay to see the outcome and made no comment about it, either then or later.

The two-week stay in Durban made me realize that the Pathers were more European than we were: in the morning they got out of bed and stayed in their pyjamas; they wore slippers; they said good morning and good night to each other and they celebrated, with fire-works, a day Indians never celebrated in the Location. When the sky-rockets were going off on that warm November night, I thought of the Location and saw in my mind's eye my "Coloured" contemporaries dressed in old outsized clothes with exaggerated bottoms and busts, and wearing outlandish make up, and singing and dancing and begging. And when Mr Pather put a crackling starlight into my hand, I thought of Ambi, Ruby and Ranga and imagined their expressions when I told them that in Durban they burnt fire-crackers not for Deepavali but for Guy Fawkes.

* * *

I was sixteen that day when I sang to myself as I walked to town, going from Jerusalem Street to Struben Street and from there to Cowie Street and then into Church Street. The words of Frankie Laine's song kept my mind off my toothache.

There was no Indian dentist in Pretoria or in the Transvaal. So I decided, since no one that I knew could recommend a white one, to go into town and search for myself. I was certain that if I went to Church Street I would find one. When I reached the Central Post Office, I paused, for it was impossible not to admire the full symmetry and the severe beauty of the Square. I had seen it so many times before but each time I reached it, the space, the order and the cleanliness was so contrary to the Location that I felt overwhelmed, intimidated and excluded. The statues of Paul Kruger and the four Voortrekkers, grim-faced and granite-like, reminded me of the history lessons at school. Paul Kruger was so valiant that he cut off his own thumb, and the Voortrekkers were so indomitable that they carved out a country and laid down a civilisation in spite of the wilderness and the savage horde.

A sign outside a building, just after Cuthberts' Shoe Store, indicated a dentist, H.M. du Plessis, on the third floor. I entered the building. The clean fresh smell made me feel nervous. I found the lift, examined the top and the sides of its entrance to see if there was a sign warning: *Europeans Only*. No, there was nothing. I was still hesitating when the doors suddenly opened. It was empty. I stepped in. I saw a row of buttons and, as I had so often seen being done in the movies, I pressed the button marked three. The doors closed and the lift, like magic, rose. On the second floor, disappointingly, it stopped. The doors opened and exposed me to a middle-aged white couple. The lift was fairly spacious but I felt more comfortable retreating to one of the far corners. The couple gave me a hard look. The man (speaking in Afrikaans) shouted: "Hey what the hell you're doing here? Don't you know, this bloody lift is for whites only? C'mon get out!"

Silent and shame-faced, I obeyed. In my anxiety to find the dentist, I had neglected an elementary rule: you only enter when it specifically says *Non-Whites Only* or *Non-Europeans Only*. Still smarting from this humiliation, I found the dentist's office. As instructed, I rang and entered.

I found a well-lit, clean and spacious room. I saw a white woman and could see, from the expression she registered on her carefully made up face, that my presence was unexpected.

"Yes? Is there something you wanted?"

"I've got a ... I'm ... I'm looking for a dentist. I have a tooth that's ... I have a tooth that's hurting me, and ..."

"No, no, no, the dentist here doesn't treat non-whites."

"Oh! Do you know where I can go? Please Madam!"

I was relieved to find that though she wasn't friendly she was at least civil.

"Farther up the street there's an entrance just before a jewelry shop — I think it's Sterns; you'll see there's two or three dentists there."

I thanked her and left. The fierce heat outside contrasted sharply with the cool air inside.

I found the building and three dentists: C. van Wyk, F.S. Brown, and A.D. Kloppers. I decided on Brown and I decided I would use the stairs. The white woman, this time, was older than the previous one but just as well groomed and manicured. She came to the point quickly: Dr Brown didn't treat non-whites; the two others didn't either.

Outside I wondered if it was worth carrying on. Somebody in the Location, I started convincing myself, must know a dentist, or know someone who knew a dentist. I was near Central Street; so I decided I might as well walk up to Andries Street and try my luck there; and sure enough I

86

found a D.M. Marais and T.S. van Zyl. I drew a blank with Marais and then entered Van Zyl's office, where I was surprised to discover a tiny room. A door in front of me opened and in came a receptionist. I explained my case, emphasizing that perhaps a filling would do.

"He'll take your tooth out but he doesn't do any fillings," she said indifferently and quizzed me with her eyes: *are you taking it or leaving it*? I hesitated but then thought, I might as well get it over and done with. So I said fatalistically, "Yes, all right Madam, I'll take it out!"

"Just go in there" —she pointed to a side door — "and he'll come and see you in a few minutes." She opened the door and, pointing to a dentist chair, said: "You can wait here." She then quietly crossed the room and left through an adjoining door.

The chair was comfortable but worn out and, here and there, the maroon leather upholstery was coming loose. Keeping my eyes on the door in front of me, I sat anxiously and waited. Suddenly the quiet calm of my wait was interrupted by the buzz of a dentist's drill. I noticed another dentist's chair in the corner. It was exactly like the one I was sitting in except that it was worse for wear and covered in dust. Basins, syringes, glasses, drawers and a set of false teeth, strewn on a corner table, were also covered in dust.

The door opened and the dentist brusquely entered. "Which one is it?" he asked in gruff Afrikaans. He did not look at me. I opened my mouth and pointed to the tooth. "Yes, I see it," he said and immediately spiked a needle into my gum. My eyes instantly became heavy with moisture. He turned around and, without a word, left as he had entered.

A few minutes later he was back — this time with a pair of forceps in his right hand. He shoved the instrument into my mouth. The action hurt the side of my mouth, but, before I could adjust to the pain, the tugging at the defective tooth had already begun. The pain, in spite of the injection, stung deep and sharp. I struggled to keep my head still but couldn't help tilting it a little; the dentist's big left hand fixed my head in a vice-like grip. The other hand followed up the wrenching action with an even fiercer resolve. The tooth, after what seemed an eternity, finally yielded. It was immediately dropped into an old waste paper basket, the blood-smeared forceps were cast on the table and banished with the other dust covered objects, and I was abandoned to what I now recognised was the storeroom. The receptionist came back, I paid and left.

I felt numb and crushed. I walked back home feeling bitter and reproached myself for not being white. When I came to Cowie Street and to the white cemetery, I couldn't help noticing the headstone of Paul Kruger's tomb. Suddenly something made me recall — it must have been the way the shade of the leaves of the tall trees fell on the ground, or the manner in which the light flicked off the top of my Jarman shoes — that when I had passed earlier, I was singing, 'On the Sunny Side of the Street'.

15

The ten-nil defeat by Rangers put paid to my career as a goal-keeper: Swaraj wasn't interested in trying me out in any other position but I was still a faithful fan, and I continued playing for Arsenal on Sunday mornings.

About a month after the defeat, Swaraj was scheduled to play Pretorians. But when the match started only nine of the eleven players had turned up. Veegee and I (he, too, after the ten-nil result was dropped) were sent home on borrowed bicycles to get togged. My uncle Anand and Bathos, the two unofficial managers of Swaraj, thought our presence would at least give the team a semblance of credibility.

Within fifteen minutes we were back and ready to go on to the field. Bathos instructed us: "Look, get in there, stay in the defence and just worry their forwards!" I didn't mind that he thought we would be nothing but scarecrow players; for I felt uninhibited. I felt I had nothing to lose. I'm sure Veegee must have felt the same way. As it happened both of us turned in impressive performances. Swaraj lost but, with a bit of luck, the result could very easily have been a draw.

From then on we became part of the permanent side. I remember I was seventeen then.

The season finished: Swaraj ended up at the bottom of the league table. Still, there was a feeling that better things were in store. Veegee and I convinced Dickie that with a few more Arsenal players Swaraj could be revitalized.

Two weeks before the official football season started Uncle Anand and Bathos thought it would be a good idea to test out the new Swaraj team: they arranged a friendly match with Fordsburg Rovers, the recent champions of the Johannesburg league. Did this Johannesburg side come without even bothering to have a few limbering up sessions before meeting us? I don't know how to explain it but we literally ran them off their feet — we beat them 14-1.

The season started and four matches and four weeks later the inevitable Swaraj-Rangers encounter took place.

* * *

The desire to beat Rangers was intense among officials, players and supporters; everywhere I went, people would say, "Best of luck for Sunday", "You've got to do it this time, boy!", "You must shut their traps this time", "Don't forget what the bastards did to Swaraj", "You've got to put them in their places on Sunday" or "You've got to teach them a lesson on Sunday that they'll never forget, man!"

For the first time, from Monday to Friday, all eleven players turned up regularly for the afternoon practice sessions. We played six-a-side football, using only a portion of the playing area.

Saturday was a rest day — a day off. I spent the day at the Market but there too I met stall owners and assistants talking about, commenting on and advising on the imminent match.

On Sunday morning there was a general-strategy talk at the house of Bathos. After the meeting somebody suggested that the players go to the Temple and pray before we returned home for lunch. Someone else warned that care should be taken to ensure that lunch wasn't too copious; someone else suggested that each player should drink a glass of milk.

I see that Sunday so clearly.

Half-past two, it was time to go. I got dressed. I put my boots on last because I was scared to lose my balance on the polished cement floor of my room. I slipped on my lumber jacket and walked quietly to the ground. The streets were deserted. It was a dry bright winter day.

I reached Barber Street and crossed the stretch of waste ground that had now turned into veld. Then I walked past a group of Zionist African Christians assembled under a sprawling thorn tree — their green lapel badges and their traffic inspector caps marked them out and gave them a quaint and fraternal look. Here and there overgrown brick and cement foundations, the debris of some of the tiny houses that used to belong to the inhabitants of Marabastad, interrupted the barren veld. The ruins conjured up a picture of a liquor raid that I had seen when I was six years old: dogs barking, white police officers directing their black subordinates, metal pikes probing the grounds of the sand yard, five gallon paraffin tins with their hold of *skokiaan* being disinterred, a hardy African woman, with her doek-covered head, looking dashed and defiant, and frail African men in handcuffs, looking cowed and woebegone, trooping down to the police station in a carnival of white might.

The ground came into view. I saw Rangers togged out in their striped jerseys and I wondered about them as individuals. Bagas, half-African half-Indian, Muslim, handsome, a real gentleman, both on and off the field. What did he do? I wasn't sure. He was always neatly dressed — always wearing a hat, must be doing some clerical work with some European company. Then there were the Moosa brothers: Issie, Hassan, Braimpie and Aggie. Issie, the eldest, it was said, worked in town as a white man. The Location had a way of saying things that sometimes had no reality. In spite of his humiliating last goal on that day when I was playing goalkeeper, I respected him; he was quiet, reserved and gentleman-like. Hassan, a junior school teacher, was also a good footballer, but not exceptional like Issie. I felt Satha, our right wing, was better than he was.

Braimpie, a school teacher, was a smooth-talking and bloody-minded right half. If he couldn't get the ball from you by hook, he'd do it just as well by crook. Aggie, unemployed, a one-time Arsenal player, was inconsistent but could at times be almost as good as Issie. Alli (Cobbler) Keshavjee, a Khoja, a nice guy but an also-ran footballer. Bharat Ramjas, a Culcuttia, a good goalkeeper, worked as a salesman for an Indian outfitter's shop. Brian Mooloo, half-"Coloured" half-Indian, a quiet, workman-like player. He had a stylish way of placing his arms whenever he kicked the ball. He worked in town for some European company — I think he was an electrician. Boerkie, a school teacher, a steady, nondescript full back. He looked like a Greek and never played dirty. Ray Singh, an efficient left half. Ebrahim Solomon, a school teacher, a quiet left winger, who was at times quite menacing. And Bapu Alli, unemployed, a tall, handsome and athletic centre half, had no intellectual grasp of the game.

Strange how football reflected life. If someone was bloody-minded on the field (like Braimpie) he'd be bloody-minded off the field; if he was fair and square on the field (like Bagas and Issie) he'd be fair and square off the field. If he was generous and playful on the field (like Dickie) he'd be generous and playful off the field.

* * *

There was an exceptionally good crowd that afternoon, and more rosettes were being worn than usual. The match opened, as if the whistle was a pistol shot and as if the players were hundred-yard runners at the starting blocks. Swaraj took control of the game early. Rangers, surprised, tried first to absorb and then to ward off the repeated forays.

After fifteen minutes Dickie picked up a loose ball and carried it up to the halfway line, he feinted and slipped a pass to me on his right. Bapu, the Rangers centre half, squared up. I made as if I were giving him the ball. He advanced to take it. With feinting foot work, I left him behind. I saw Satha on the right and Veegee on the left, and sensed Dickie coming up fast from behind. I positioned myself to pass to Satha; this drew Alli Cobbler wide. I turned left and inward, and was in line for a pass to Veegee. I feinted a pass and pulled Brian Mooloo out of the way. I then tapped the ball, with calculated weight, into the gap. Dickie, as anticipated, picked it up on his run and smacked it first time with his right instep. The ball screeched along the ground and went full pelt into the far corner of the net. One nil. The Swaraj supporters enthused and buzzed. On the Rangers side of the ground there was a grave-like silence.

The goal transformed the Swaraj game: pass after pass,

swift, short and decisive multiplied. A sparkling sheen settled over their play. Tackles were blessed, passes were elected and attacks were sanctified. Those dissolute punts into the void, those pray-to-God and mother-help-us kicks — the grace of Location full backs and the bane of good play — were kept to a minimum.

Satha broke past two players on the right and darted towards the corner, as if he was iron and the corner flag lodestone, before he sent his pass across. Everyone, including Veegee, expected a lob or a volley but the ball came in low, skidding along the surface. Veegee missed it, Alli Cobbler missed it, Bharat, the goalkeeper, missed it: I, in desperation, lunged at it, feet first, and just managed to touch it with the toe of my right boot — it was hardly elegant, but unbelievably, it curved and spun towards the goal, and violently swished against the inside net before it came to a halt. Two nil.

Half time. Swaraj came off feeling that the match was under control. Uncle Anand, aglow with satisfaction, greeted them: "Another forty-five minutes like that, boys, and tonight we'll celebrate." Bathos, his face betraying that his liver was a bedfellow of Rembrandt brandy, said more prosaically: "Boys, you've got them by the balls, squeeze them, smash them!" Vella, a keen supporter, had a bag of oranges in his hand. He removed the oranges, one by one, and rolled them towards the players like bowling balls. The Zebediela oranges came in helter-skelter, colliding against our thighs and legs. The winter sun cast dark weird elongated shadows across the playing surface. Ten- and twelve-year olds milled around, fixing their eyes on us, as if we were ten feet tall. Every now and then they leapt to recover the spent oranges that were hurriedly squeezed and sucked dry, and then carelessly cast aside. Dickie, his glistening face beaming like Burt Lancaster's in *Vera Cruz*, winked at me. I smiled and said, "No ten nil today." Veegee, grinning like Jerry Lewis, said: "Heh huh, heh, this is it, huh! We got them today, Joe!" Satchoo, always prudent and naturally endowed with a businessman's caution, said: "Don't count chickens before they are hatched!"

The second half, like the first, started at a crackling pace. But now the enthusiasm of the crowd was redoubled: they forsook the makeshift seats made of raw tree trunks and stood on the sacred touch-line, and, like the wash of the tide on a beach, infringed it each time play was away and heeded it each time it came back; nudging each other after every successful dribble or pass, and punctuating each gesture with: "How's that, man?" "Hey!" "Just watch that, boy!" and "How do you like that for a hommle?" A rite of communion, an uncanny communication, established itself between players and supporters. Every tackle, every dribble, every pass, every shot, every success and every failure was felt, given collective expression, regretted and hosannaed on the touch-line.

Dickie tackled Bagas and deprived him of the ball. He moved forward, as if out on a Sabbath stroll; the Rangers defence, and even some of the Swaraj forwards, thought the referee had stopped play. He changed pace from five to fifty miles an hour, passed Bapu and Braimpie and spotted Veegee readying himself to dash through the gap created in the centre. He turned and chipped the ball over the head of the advancing Brian. Veegee, just inside the penalty area, met it with a volley. The ball flashed and entered the goal like a missile. Three nil.

Rangers were on the point of giving up. There was more to the pleasure of football than just goals. It was time to tease. Dickie had possession. Bapu came forward. Dickie told him (using body and foot language): "Well, what are you waiting for? Come and get it!" Dickie disarmed the ball, left it exposed in front of his immobile feet, offered it like a Good Samaritan. "Take it!" he urged, using the same language. Tempted, and hoping to clear the ball with the tip of his boot, Bapu plunged forward with a dive tackle. There are times, rare but real, when the Goddess of football graces absolutely; whatever stroke or trick tried, it would somehow be sanctified, solemnized, beatified. Dickie drew the ball away, as if it was glued to the sole of his boot. His immobile left foot was framed by the Rangers player's outstretched legs. He disengaged his left foot, slowly and exaggeratedly, and then moved on. To the cheering and whooping crowd it was Daniel cowing the lion.

He closed towards Alli Cobbler, who came down on him like Goliath. He moved to the left and flicked the ball to Veegee on the right; and, anticipating the momentum of Cobbler's desperate lunge, He stepped aside to avoid the unnecessary clash of bodies. Veegee, now in possession, continued the tease. The Swaraj supporters loved it and wanted more.

Satha duly gave them a fourth goal.

In the dying minutes of the game, Rangers, like Philistines looking upon their crumbling temple, watched the ball go from one Swaraj player to another.

As soon as the match ended James Karia Kollapen, the tough, dagga-smoking Delfos centre half and star — he couldn't stand the Rangers side — dashed on to the field, swept Dickie off his feet and hoisted him on to his shoulders. He then paraded him and unblushingly sang his praises: "What a match! What a match you played there! What a match!"

16

She wore a plain, collarless, black dress. I was surprised to discover how the black sheen of the dress's fabric set off her brown eyes and her ruby lips. After she had entered, I bolted the door behind her. She turned and smiled. Hardly any words were spoken. She looked at me with an expression of quiet expectation. I advanced and kissed her full but softly on her lips. I found her hand, switched the light off and led her to the bed in the far corner. Soon we were stretched out on the covers lying on our sides, fully dressed, kissing and caressing each other. Our lips became hungrier and our hands more determined but there was an undeclared understanding that our clothes would never come off and our hands would never touch forbidden flesh.

Soobathie had befriended my sister, Ambi, and came, ostensibly, to see her at 226. But late in the evening, when nobody but Ambi was aware, she slipped into the room next door, where I impatiently awaited her.

I encouraged her to roll over on to her back; I eased myself on to her. The intensity of the darkness in the room fell and the evening light, entering through the small high window, provided a shadowy visibility. I saw the ball ricocheting off my boot and go curling away into the net. My floating gaze fell on the LP covers plastering one of the walls: Neil Sedaka, Gene Vincent, Pat Boone, Jerry Lee Lewis; it stopped when it came to Elvis Presley. I saw images of 'Love Me Tender' and a sharp close up of Debra Paget. Yes, there was something in Soobathie that reminded me of her. I wondered what it was.

Soobathie, breathing softly now, had her head on my chest. I thought I felt moisture seeping through my shirt and on to my chest. Was she crying? I gently lifted her head. I saw her

96

face, as if in a faded photograph, misty and enchanting.

I moved my hand gently over her cheeks and towards her eyes, and resolved, if they were tears, to brush them aside, but then I thought better of it. I pulled her up and started kissing her affectionately and endearingly on her eye lashes and on her eye lids. She lifted her head and, as if to thank me, kissed me hard and wet. The urge to make love welled up again, but the delicate dampness spreading on my shirt front transformed passion into anxiety.

"Did I hurt you?"

"No! no!"

"What's wrong then?"

"C'mon tell me, Soobie!"

"My mother says some Germiston people are coming to talk girl for their son. And they're coming in two weeks time to ask for me."

"Do you know the guy?"

"No, no. It's the first time I've heard of him."

I felt aggrieved and irritated. "Well, tell your mum about us. Tell her we've been seeing each other. Tell her we're serious!"

"I'll try!"

I got up and put the light on. She asked me, almost in a whisper, to get her a glass of water and to call Ambi. When Ambi entered the room, I went out into the spare and sparse room that was used for ironing — and waited. A minute or so later Ambi came out with the black dress in her hand.

* * *

When I met Soobathie again, I was dismayed to learn that her mother had pooh-poohed my good intentions. She had told Soobathie, blankly, that a bird in the hand was worth two in the bush.

I spent a disquieting Sunday night: I could hardly sleep. Monday night was no better. I couldn't stand the thought of losing Soobathie. I liked everything I knew about her. Why this menace to our relationship when we were just starting to get to know each other? Who anyway was this bloody guy from Germiston?

On Tuesday I was sitting on the stoep. It was just after two p.m. Jerusalem Street was fairly animated, buses swept past and people drifted by in a steady flow. I sat, sullen and despondent, in the basket armchair. Mother came out and sat in the armchair beside me. She silently watched the street. We sat there for a little while in total silence, as if we were strangers waiting for a bus, but I felt her presence, she felt mine. Every now and then she turned her head and looked in my direction. After a while she said nonchalantly: "You look as if you've got troubles."

I was surprised to discover that my face betrayed the troubled thoughts that my brain and heart were harbouring. Maybe I was waiting for her to enquire and maybe I wanted her to see me troubled. Whatever the case, I didn't hesitate to tell her what was eating me.

"It's up to you," she said blandly. "I can go and see her parents and ask them for house permission — if that is what you want?"

I looked at her, hesitated for a second or two, and then surprised myself by nodding assent. She eyed me with a I-wish-I-could-sometimes-say-no-to-you look, rose and said, "I'm going to get dressed."

The sari she was wearing used to be a bright-coloured Madras check but wear and repeated washings had rendered it pale and threadbare. Ten or fifteen minutes later she came back. Her face was freshly washed. She gave off a faint scent of soap and talc. Her long, thick, black hair was severely combed back and the ends were bunched and neatly twisted into a bun at the back of her head. Her diamond *mookoutie* caught the sunlight and reflected a golden sparkle across the shaded window pane. Her plain blue sari, which looked as if she was wearing it for the first time, was covered with a gold braid.

"Are you ready?" she asked teasingly. When we were out on the street she said, without looking at me, "You know, you deserve better." I didn't say anything. I thought of the other possibilities in the Location. There was the Moosa's sister, Juki. She looked and behaved like a European. But she was older than me and, besides, she belonged to the Location's aristocracy. She'd never even bothered to look at me. She was definitely out of my league. Then there was Tanga, one of the Chetty Brothers' daughters, but she, too, was an aristocrat, her family had the money to prove it: they owned the Orient cinema, had a wholesale grocery business and ran a café; and, anyway, she was already engaged to some rich, Durban bloke. Sure, I'd prefer Debra Paget, Rossana Podesta, Debbie Reynolds, Kim Novak or Jean Simmons but I knew they were goddesses and, whatever my mother might think, I was neither Greek nor God.

The only other girl who could have rivalled Soobathie's beauty was her younger sister, Rajas, but she was haughty and pretentious. Maybe in Nigel or in some of the other obscure places like Germiston, Boksburg, Brits, Benoni, Standerton, Witbank or Springs there might be some undiscovered beauty. But, as was often said, beauty was only skin deep. I didn't want to run the risk of having beauty accompanied by naïveté. I didn't want a plaas girl for a life-long companion. Besides, these rural, small-dorp girls had a disconcerting way of lacing their Tamil, never mind their English, with Afrikaans.

We turned down Grand Street. It was impossible not to notice the posters outside the cinema. Glenn Ford in *The Sheepman*. Ah, I thought, I'm sure I'm going to like that. He was superb in *The Fastest Gun Alive*. What about next week? Hitchcock. *Vertigo*. Ah, it'll really be good to see one of his films again. Pictures of Farley Granger in *The Rope*, and *Strangers on a Train*; James Stewart in *Rear Window*; Montgomery Clift in *I Confess*; Gary Grant in *To Catch a Thief*; and Henry Fonda in *The Wrong Man* all flicked through my mind's eye.

The contact of the sole of my shoe with a stray stone shook me out of my reverie. I looked down and saw the suede uppers of my veld shoes covered in light dust. A black Chevrolet on the side of the street, which hadn't moved for a day or two, was covered in a film of red dust. The skeletal jacaranda tree nearby was also covered in dust. Just ahead and above, my eyes fell on the roof of the building that housed Tip Top Press and there, too, a thick layer of dust covered the red-painted, corrugated iron roofing. My throat felt suddenly irritated and I wanted to cough.

We approached the corner of Sixth Street. I felt strange walking past the Corner with my mother at my side. The last time we walked together here was when she tried to take me to school. I hoped Innie or Veegee or Butcher or any of the other guys weren't around. They would wonder what was up when they saw me going down Grand Street like this. The bastards would be bound to put two and two together and come up with house permission.

We reached the house. I immediately noticed that Soobathie's mother, a tiny woman who had a head like a chicken and a voice like a crow, was looking smirkily self-satisfied. A social call like this, couldn't be anything but the beginning of marriage negotiations — the implications of our visit suddenly dawned on me. But I was too excited and anxious to consider any further. There was polite talk in Tamil. Then Soobathie's mother went to the back of the yard to fetch her husband. His African employees, who hawked vegetables and fruit for him in a horse-drawn cart, had just got back. I heard the busy sounds of outspanning and off-loading filtering in from the yard.

The front room of the house, the sitting room, was medium sized, clean, tidy and tasteless; the curtains and the greenish walls were drab, and the furniture was nondescript. The only thing remarkable was the passage way into the other rooms, it was doorless and draped with a full-length curtain.

Soobathie's father joined us. It was obvious she had inherited her good looks from him. He had a round face, a pinched nose, aggressive eyebrows and eyes, quick nervous movements and a hurried and coarse high-pitched voice. My mother provided the necessary assurance: an engagement and, ultimately, a wedding once house permission had been granted. Soobathie's father turned to me and jovially asked me what I aimed to do.

I wasn't quite expecting this question. I knew I didn't want to end up in the Market. I wasn't interested in studying. Mother, I was aware, wanted me to become a teacher. I

100

myself liked the idea of dressing up well, looking neat and presentable but teachers had already by then acquired the reputation of being drinkers — drink like a teacher was a current expression. Rich parents, who could read and write, steered their offspring into the lucrative avenues of law and medicine. I didn't think I had the brain or the stamina to go beyond matric, and no one tried to persuade me otherwise. I wasn't quite sure what I wanted to do. The best I could think of at that moment was to be a clerk in some European business. I wrote neatly, was OK at figures and wasn't bad at writing compositions — I'd be able to write a business letter. Anyway I saw myself as a no-dirty-hands worker; so I said: "Oh, I'm thinking of passing my matric first and then I'll probably get a job as a clerk with some firm in town."

That visibly satisfied him and his spouse. I had unwittingly impressed them with my seriousness. My priority of matric over work, of down-to-earth, nothing-fancy work, did the trick. Some general talk followed, while tea in cups and saucers that obviously had come out of the show case and assorted Three Rings biscuits were served. Husband and wife then expatiated upon how a tin of sardines in their day had cost a penny and now cost 1/6, "but you see wages since then has gone up, so really it's more or less the same thing." They were pleased with themselves for being able to formulate such a sophisticated economic idea. I feigned innocence and, with a well-now-I've-really-learnt-something expression on my face, indicated that I had been suitably impressed. Soobathie did the service. Through the corner of my eyes I could see she was radiant but we carried on as if we were complete strangers.

* * *

House permission was marvellously emancipatory; for from then on, while we still had to be discreet, there was no need to duck and dive. I recall now how the days that separated Sunday from that fateful Tuesday were as long as weeks. When Sunday eventually came it was barely possible to wait for that moment when the two of us would be alone.

101

Soobathie came wearing a pink woollen cardigan with turned-up collars and a cotton dress with buttons all along the front. She was as sparkling and as beautiful as ever, but I noticed there was a glint of decisiveness and assurance in her look that simply wasn't there before.

The full kiss, the grasp of the hand and the switching off of the light had become a ritual, but as I led her to the bed she halted and said, "Is it all right if I take my dress off. Poor Ambi has to iron it each time we finish here; if I take it off now, it won't get creased."

It was still too dark to see exactly how she was taking off her dress but the distinct sounds of unbuttoning and the soft swishing sounds of material folding and straightening out, the music of undressing, warmed my blood and rushed my pulse. When my hand touched her naked shoulder an emotional charge ran through my body. I unbuttoned my shirt. I had on a pair of blue jeans but I had taken care to remove my brass-buckled leather belt before she had entered the room.

The skin-to-skin contact with her back and her midriff revealed, for the first time, the secret pleasures of a woman's body, pleasures that I had only dimly suspected.

17

Uncle Nades's Café, three blocks away from Jerusalem Street and within a stone's throw of the Tamil School, used to be a butcher's shop. Uncle Nades was never there. He had a grocery shop in Blood Street and he lived in the dead-end part of Grand Street, the same street as his café.

Opposite the Café, moving clockwise, was the zinc and wooden house where Dickie Moodley, his two brothers and his widowed mother lived. Their house was one among many making up the complex of Scotland Yard, the block between Sixth and Cowie Streets, where about ninety people lived. Just one block farther down Grand Street, between Cowie and Eighth Streets, another stand housed even more people. Oddly enough this Cowie Street place had no name. Perhaps, this was so because it was more recent. Scotland Yard was Scotland Yard before I was even born, but the Cowie-Street place used to be a second and rival Tamil school and prayer centre — Tamil cultural affairs always produced its schisms.

One day this second Tamil school, in the style of a large Spanish-American house with a spacious inner court open to the sky, had its classrooms transformed into boarding rooms, and it too thereafter became a collective habitation. Butcher's family and another seventy-six people lived there, and they (like those of Scotland Yard) shared a single toilet and bathroom. It must have been this dual and double concentration of Tamil homes that gave the Corner its reputation of being the centre of Tamil-land.

Adjoining Dickie's home, was Matthew's place. Matthew, a lean, tired-looking man with a Hitler moustache and a Dravidian tint, was a Tamil Christian. He worked as a waiter. It's strange but nearly all the Tamil Christians were waiters.

103

There was something about them, I don't know what it was exactly, that made them generous and likeable. Matthew didn't say much. Come to think of it, I don't think I ever heard him say anything. He was married to a "Coloured" woman, who had a fair complexion but a turned-up nose and a great fat shape. He had four children, who all resembled her more than they did him. Living space at his place was even more cramped than it was at the Moodley's. Matthew, giving the impression of being a mere boarder, seemed not to belong to the house.

The house opposite Matthew's place was more elaborate. It had a waist-high brick wall enclosing a large stoep. This brick wall, with its ledge, provided the seats and the cosiness of much morning and evening conversations and idle talk. Auntie Jaytoon, the Malay woman who owned the house, was subdued, frail and widowed. There were quite a few widowed women in the Location. Auntie Jaytoon was never without her doek. She had three grown-up children: two boys and one girl. Toya, her younger son, once tried to settle in Germany but he didn't make it. He seemed to be one of those guys who never make it in anything. Frieda, about five years older than myself, had thick long hair and full lips.

Auntie Jaytoon made and sold koeksisters. On Sunday mornings I used to go down to Tenth Street to buy the *Sunday Times*, the *Sunday Express* and the *Golden City Post* and on my way back I would stop at Auntie Jaytoon's, enter the yard and queue outside the tiny dark kitchen, where the heavy aroma of hot syrup and coconut smothered the air.

Adjoining the Jaytoon's place, curving into Sixth Street (the Jaytoon place was dead in the corner), was where Innie, his two brothers and sister (the doyenne of the family) lived. Innie's family was special. Shushila — everybody called her Suzy — was a junior school teacher, real sophisticated, light-skinned, spoke like a *laanie*, was, actually, more European than the Europeans. She didn't figure much in Location life, for she married a Prinsloo-Street millionaire and moved to Johannesburg.

Nanand, his brother, two or three years older than myself,

looked like Frank Sinatra. Everybody called him Bootch. Why? I don't know. Bootch couldn't sing for love or money, but he was very suave. Like so many in the Location he left school early. He never, thereafter, did a stroke of work. He stuttered but had, for all that, the gift of the gab. There was something about him — an oddity equivalent to the humour of a court jester that made him a favourite of the rich and easy. He was always hanging around one of the Orient brothers. From time to time you'd see him appear with a spanking new outfit: a zoot suit, a cut-away collar shirt, a broad brocaded tie with a zoot knot, a two-tone pair of Flosheim shoes and a Dobson hat. He'd sport the outfit everyday until it started wearing out, then he'd either abandon it or continue wearing it until it was unwearable; or until once again he got himself, in some mysterious way, another new outfit.

The elder brother, Nades, was six years older than Innie. He played for Delfos, although he had originally been a Swaraj player. He was a pretty good footballer. He read the game well but he was (like Innie) a bit of a squealer: he couldn't stand being in the wrong or being deprived of the ball. He was, like so many young and intelligent Tamils, a junior school teacher; and, I suppose, he was the only one in Tamil-land who was an intellectual — he looked like Jack Palance. Every time I saw him I couldn't help thinking of that scene in *The Sign of the Pagan*, where Jack Palance, playing the role of Atilla the Hun, on being asked to name himself as he enters a meeting of chiefs, exclaims: "Name myself? Name myself, he says!" Nades's intimate friends — Dickie for instance — called him, Palance.

Across the Street, opposite the Jaytoon place, was the Fischer home. It's strange but I never did have the curiosity to want to know why Khrishnaner's brother was called Fischer. The house, a brick structure with a corrugated iron roof, was modest and comfortable. Gona (one of Fischer's three sons) lived there. Gona was my hero. He really was an outstanding goalkeeper. He had big hands, big shoulders, a broad face, a husky voice and a belly-full of guts. One of his favourite saves was to dive at the feet of onrushing forwards. He captained Delfos, represented Pretoria and played for the

Transvaal. It was unfortunate that the Durban team had a one-eyed goalkeeper called Sam Moodley. Sam was even more of a daredevil than Gona. Sometimes I wondered if Sam wasn't a *dagga-rooker*, for his temerity was second to none. Anyway Sam barred Gona's way to a South African selection, preventing him from becoming an Indian Springbok. Dickie, had it not been for Gona, would have been my hero. But Dickie was physically frail, whereas no one, on or off the field, could intimidate Gona.

Gona was also my photographic mentor. He taught me everything there was to know about photography. I always remember how he once told me that it made no sense to take photos of a building, a scene or a monument if someone didn't figure in it. "If you want a picture of the Union Buildings, just by itself, it's better to buy a postcard. Postcards are professional products. But if you want to take a picture of the Union Buildings to mark the fact that you, your friends or your family visited it on a certain day, it's better to get yourself, or them, and the building on the same photo — otherwise what's the point of owning a camera?"

Gona was also political in a strangely apolitical way. He never once explained why he opposed the Government. He just opposed it on the assumption that it was evil. To me this opposition seemed to be a sort of game, where the object was to twit the legal authorities. Sometimes you'd be there standing and chatting with him; he'd be there leaning, with the palm of his hand on an electric pole, and when, the exchange over, you stepped aside to continue your way, you'd notice a sticker reading: *Stay at home*, or some other similar contestation, positioned exactly where his hand had been.

The Corner, although I wasn't aware of it, was my university. One day Nades, Gona, Dickie and a few other big guys were discussing some matter. Butcher, Innie, Veegee and I were there half listening to their talk when all at once the word maintenance was uttered. Soobia (one of the conservative, temple-going big guys) thought the word shouldn't have been mentioned in front of us *lightees*. Nades thought the caution unwarranted. He turned towards us and said: "Hey

106

fellas, do you know what maintenance means?" All of us, I think, shook our heads in a joint admission of ignorance.

"Ah well, it simply means the money a man pays to a woman he has left or divorced for the upkeep of their kids."

Well, thanks to Nades I added another word to my vocabulary. But he always had interesting things to say — at least, things that made you think.

One afternoon Nades was standing outside the Café, leaning against the wall, just outside the door and sipping a small Coke. I was seated on an empty cold drink box, with my back against one of the many pillars of the stoep. I needed to take out my handkerchief and as I did so a tickey dropped out of my pocket and rolled across the cement surface towards Nades's feet. I didn't for some reason notice the loss. Nades picked up the coin, came over to me and said, as he handed it back to me, "Hey, you've lost this!" I acknowledged his gesture with a look of gratitude and sheepishly added: "I must have lost it when I took my handkerchief out."

"Well, I'm honest, am I not?" he twinkled. I could see he was teasing me.

"Ja, of course, you're honest, sir" — that sir bit was something the Location accorded all qualified teachers.

"Yes, but imagine you had lost a £1000 or £10,000. I might have been tempted to keep it. I'm honest when it is a tickey but would I have been honest if it had been a £1000?"

This observation exercised me. The words relative or subjective did not occur to me but the idea that moral values were self-serving fascinated me.

It was also at Uncle Nades's Café that Saripath (who lived in Jerusalem Street, and who was twice Nades's age) gave out that one drop of squirt was the equivalent of twenty drops of blood. This intelligence scared me for a time but then I learnt, also from the same fountain of knowledge, that a good helping of *doppeas* and milk, or milk and mashed avocado, instantaneously replaced the lost semen. From that day on I became hooked on peanuts and avocados.

Whether it was the MCC to play cricket, the Lions, the All Blacks or the Wallabies to play rugby, Newcastle United,

107

Motherwell, Spurs or the England Football Association Eleven to play football, the Location always — always — backed the visiting team. One day during a test match series between the MCC and the white national team, Nades proposed that we should back not the visiting team but the local white team. Gona, Dickie and some others greeted this proposal with surprise and a chorus of derision.

"Hey, what's wrong with you?" Gona challenged. "You're talking nonsense, man. Hey Nades, how are you man?"

"Look, there's apartheid, and there's whites only this, and whites only that — OK, but the whites are after all South Africans. We are South Africans. These MCC fellows come from England. When our Pretoria boys play against the Jo'burg fellows we kooza our boys, not the Jo'burg fellows. Well, don't we?"

Gona and the others taken aback, and at a loss for words, just shook their heads. I thought, yes but these overseas whites are better than the whites here. I knew from my Market experience that the overseas whites were more polite and less contemptuous of us than were the local whites, but, even so, Nades's words gave me, as the Location would say, food for thought.

* * *

Football, at the Corner, was nearly always played with a tennis ball. Every now and then, non-white cops used to chase us *lightees*, confiscate our ball and, sometimes, take us down to the police station and charge us for obstructing and hindering traffic. One late afternoon, Innie, Butcher, Veegee and I were playing controllings, kicking about an old tennis ball when Butcher spied a young African cop coming up Grand Street. "Arra! arra!" he shouted. Everyone scattered and disappeared into the different yards. But the precious ball was deserted, abandoned. I hesitated, recovered the ball, went around the Jaytoon house and entered Sixth Street and then, realizing that I'd be involved in a vulgar and vain chase, I decided I'd duck behind the walls of the Jaytoon's stoep. I gripped the ledge with my left hand, cleared the wall

108

with a sideways somersault, broke my fall with my right hand, and landed softly and tightly against the blind side of the wall. Unfortunately, the cop must have had time enough to spot my feet going over the top of the wall; otherwise he would have rounded the house and discovered that he had lost me.

A heavy hand grabbed my collar and pulled me up smartly. My fourteen-year-old heart beat like the pistons of a racing car in full throttle. The policeman, intimidating me with his uniform and his authority, did not say anything, but his manner indicated that he was about to march me down to the police station.

Frieda came out from within the house. Innie, Butcher and Veegee, pretending to be mere bystanders, appeared. Nades also appeared. He addressed the policeman in Afrikaans, which he spoke as impeccably as he did English.

"Hey, leave the youngster alone! There's better things for a policeman to do than go about arresting children playing football in the streets!"

The young policeman did not notice that a small hostile crowd had gathered. The policeman, by this time, had me perched on the ledge of the wall and, using his right hand, held me tightly by the wrist. Frieda came up from behind and put her arms around me and held me tightly against her chest in a gesture of protection and defiance.

I felt, even in my anxiety and fear, the generous warmth and softness of her breasts. It was the first time — I was fourteen then and yet to meet Soobie — I had been so closely embraced by a woman. Never before was I so delicately balanced between fear and pleasure.

Nades went on berating the inexperienced policeman: "Where do you expect the kids to play, if not in the streets? C'mon leave him alone and go and occupy your time with better things!"

It was true, we played in the street because there wasn't anywhere else to play. There was no park and no play grounds anywhere and even the football ground was often closed — on Fridays, for instance, when the playing surface was freshly marked, it was completely out of bounds. Sure, we sometimes braved the fence and played on the ground without permission but then we risked having our ball confiscated by the "ground boys".

The policeman, wearing a look which betrayed doubt and insecurity, sensed that it would be rash to persist with the arrest. In a thin act of bravado he took his notebook out and demanded Nades's name and address. Nades, undaunted, complied but with a contempt that was scarcely veiled. The policeman retreated with his tail between his legs.

* * *

A few days after the final against Rangers, Boot Gamer greeted me: "That was a grand match on Sunday. You fellas must keep it up." And then he added, almost as if his words were a pat on the back: "You play good football."

Praise, coming from him, made my day.

Whenever I saw Boot Gamer, I was perplexed and troubled He was half-Indian half-"Coloured" and worked as a waiter. Physically, he was reed-thin but on the field his skeletal figure was somehow forgotten. When I first saw him playing, I was in short pants; later, when I was playing in the first division with Swaraj, he was still playing for Delfos and for the Pretoria eleven. He was one of the stars of Location football; anybody who knew anything about football knew Boot Gamer. He was one of those rare players that did everything with precision and grace, everything with a soft deft touch. He was a true prince on the field, yet off the field he was nothing, a nonentity. I couldn't come to terms with this disparity. Football and life were one. How could someone with so much talent on the field be simply no one off the field?

A tennis ball was being kicked about. Boot Gamer, Tilak (another football star of the Location), Nades and Karia were loosely grouped in a circle. The tiny ball came to Boot Gamer. He lifted it with his left foot in a scooping movement, tapped it with the sole of his mocassin (like a tennis player sometimes taps the ball against the ground with his racket before serving), flicked his ankle in a jack-knife movement and hit the ball with the soft instep of his foot. The ball soared into the air at a ninety degree angle. He turned his head skyward, eyed the ball and then, on its downward plunge and with the instep of his moccasin, caught it dead in a swing. It was done neat and clean, done with perfection.

Boot Gamer really knew how to talk to the ball. He was a past master of these street-corner football jam sessions. How I regret now that I didn't go up to him and say, like a mantra to one of the Hindu Gods: "Boot Gamer, you're a great player! Boot Gamer, you're a great player! Boot Gamer, you're a great player!"

The ball left Boot Gamer's foot and came to me — an invitation to join in. I copied his movements. I tapped the ball against the tarred surface, hit it softly into the air at a ninety degree angle and, instead of dropping it (like Boot Gamer did) passed it, with my knee, on to my football Guru but at the last moment I straightened my leg (like a reverse flick of a jack-knife) and recovered what I had pretended to forsake. I then headed the ball softly to Nades. Boot Gamer was too experienced to be duped by my feint, he wasn't *fished*; but he appreciated the trick, for he smiled and said, "You almost got me there, Henna!"

Nades, after receiving the ball, brought it under control and then provided a performance of his own speciality before passing it on to Tilak. Tilak did the same and then passed it on to Karia. And so the ball went round. Everyone watched the player in possession and everyone appreciated the ingenuity of his repertoire and applauded the virtuoso of his performance.

I think, I enjoyed these footballing get-togethers even more than real football.

* * *

Two weeks later I was at Nades's Café. I sat on an empty cold drink box. Innie, sitting on one of the steps on the threshold of the Café, whistled an improvised version of 'The Falling Leaves'. Next to him, Bangat (a Calcuttia) was leaning against the wall and staring into the void. It was a hot languid afternoon.

111

Artee appeared, as if from nowhere.

I knew Artee by sight and as a prospective "Coloured" teacher. He was dark-skinned, tall, square-jawed and extremely well-built. I wondered why he was looking so grim and merciless. Bangat, locked in his day dreams, didn't at first notice him, but in an instant the two were face to face and eyeball to eyeball.

Bangat, slightly shorter than Artee, looked frail and anxious. Artee, a menace in flesh, unzipped the brown leather lumber jacket he was wearing and, in a wild movement, tore it off and flung it on to the cement floor. He squared up to Bangat and, as he did so, he shouted out (in Afrikaans): "Defend yourself, you bastard!"

Bangat hesitated, whirled round, cut the corner and fled. Artee gave chase but Bangat, the lighter of the two, was fleeter. Opposite the Royal cinema on a derelict patch of waste ground, two of Artee's friends lay in wait. Bangat practically ran into them before he saw his predicament. Innie and I, almost without wanting to, followed the explosion of movements. We found ourselves standing on the embankment of the Cinema, looking directly on to the patch where the two men confronted each other once again.

Artee threw out the same defiance; except, this time, he added the word, *bangbroek*.

Bangat, motionless and mute, resigned himself to his fate, but his eyes, like that of a forlorn cat's, pleaded for mercy. Artee's eyes were filled with hatred. Artee methodically directed hard heavy blows to Bangat's face. Blow after blow, sounding like the cracking of a sjambok, landed mercilessly on Bangat's face. Each assault cut, split and transformed whole into parts, flesh into blood. Yet, oddly, Bangat made no attempt to defend himself. He did not duck, he did not turn away, he did not raise his arms — he just stood there and accepted the punishment in total silence.

I can't say I liked Bangat, though I admired his courage, that is, on the football field. He didn't flinch from tackling anyone, no matter how big or tough, and, what's more, his tackles were fierce and full-blooded and, though not always successful, at least, off-putting and galling. I had on one occasion, however, felt sorry for him. It was during a school-sports, practice session when he attempted a high jump. He had cleared the bar but landed on his elbow. I remember the sick sight of the dislocation: I cringed at the thought that his bone, positioned so grotesquely, might at any moment pierce the skin. But his reaction then, as now, was mute and impassive.

On another occasion, on a quiet Sunday afternoon, I was sitting on the wall of Auntie Jaytoon's stoep, when Bangat (by this time he had long since left School) and about eight of his ruffian friends, of whom Jack Slyce was the most notorious, descended Grand Street. It was clear that they had had too much to drink and that they were out for mischief. When I spotted them, I hesitated and wondered whether I should remain seated or disappear. I half persuaded myself that since I knew Bangat, and Jack Slyce, I wouldn't be molested. Just then an African, evidently a stranger to the Location, passed Nades's Café and crossed their path. Innocent of their reputations and of their presence, he passed nonchalantly in front of their very noses. One of the gang, with a sweeping foot movement, clumsily succeeded in tripping the unfortunate stranger. Taken unawares, he fell lightly, got up instantaneously and, in spite of his obvious bewilderment, became aware of the menace facing him. But in the meanwhile a drunken kick caught him on the side of the hip and a punch grazed him near the ear. More astonished than pained, the man had wit enough to bolt. Bangat and his cohorts, fortunately, were in no condition to effect a chase.

I might have been their next victim, if Frieda had not stepped out on to the stoep and dragged me off the wall, and into the house. She reprimanded: "You can't sit there, they'll beat you up!" Embarrassed and pleased, I smiled and thought of that day when I had her big breasts against my back.

But Bangat was capable of worse. One night during a drunken brawl in a quiet part of Cowie Street, he stabbed and killed two innocent and harmless Africans. He was arrested and tried, but bribery got him off scot-free.

Even so, now I felt extremely sorry for him, but at the same time, I told myself, he must have done something really awful to have aroused such vicious anger in Artee. I wanted the beating to end. I wished for an intervention by Superman or Zorro but I realized these heroes wouldn't deign to come to our God-forsaken Location. I then, more realistically, wished that a policeman or some venerable person of the Location would intervene. But although a crowd had gathered, no one did. I was too young, too remote, too weak and too frightened to do anything but wonder and be sick. Not being able to stand any more of it, I walked away feeling guilty, hopeless and ashamed that such violence was possible and that so many were prepared to watch, as if it was a football match or a circus performance. I think it was that day more than any other which made me want to get away from the Location for good and all.

How did it stop? When did it stop? I never found out. A few days later I saw Bangat, his normally yellow complexion, which came from an excess of dagga smoking, was black and blue all over. Strips of elastic plaster dramatized his disfigurement. Yet, bad as the signs were, I was surprised to find that the damage hadn't been worse. In the first place, I was astonished to see that he was all in one piece. As I looked at him, I couldn't help wondering what fate lay in store for Artee. I felt certain that only half the drama had been played out. Bangat, after all, had ruthless friends; besides, revenge in the Location was as natural as mulberries.

A week or so later I saw Artee walking down Grand Street. He bore no signs of injury, no plaster or bandage scarred his face. I was dumbfounded. Perhaps, Bangat had merited what he had got and he himself had recognised the legitimacy of the chastisement — that's why he didn't try to defend himself, that's why no revenge was taken. Artee came nearer and passed close by. His jaw, I noticed, was wired up.

18

The relationship between Saturdays and the Market, ever since I was eleven years old, became fixed like dust is to drought. My mother told me that my father, before he met her, used to sell bottles and bags in a push cart. I couldn't imagine him recovering jute bags and empty paraffin bottles at a throw-away price and then selling them to some small wholesaler at a slightly less throw-away price. I saw him as a Market stall owner, permanently and exclusively.

"Is this first grade?"

"Yes sir, look for yourself!" I pointed to the blue ticket attached to the bag of potatoes. The white customer gave me that distrustful and disdainful look which so vexed me, and which I always took to mean: "Do you expect me to believe a born cheat like you?"

"I assure you, sir, this is first grade potatoes!" I detested the idea of having to empty out the thirty-seven pound bag of potatoes and then having to refill it again but, with a touch of bravado, I said, "I don't mind emptying it out for you, if that is what you want, sir." Fortunately, the *laanie* was convinced; he bought the potatoes. Boy, how I could sometimes hate the Market.

In the central lane of the Market, diagonally opposite my father's stall, was Fara's stall. Fara was a Muslim. I often thought about the way we Indians were divided: Tamils, Calcuttias, Muslims and Hindus. And then divided again: the Tamils into Naidoos, Moodleys, Pillays, Padyachees, Reddys, Govenders, Pathers and Kollopens; the Calcuttias into Singhs, Mooloos and Rahs; the Muslims into Koknies, Memons, Surtees, Kannemias, Khojas and Malays; and the Hindus into Joshies, Kalyans, Bhanas and Patels.

Fara was a Kannemia. He was handsome, with a square face and a full forehead; his Tony Curtis hairstyle was one of the best in the Location. He reminded me of the South African actor, Lawrence Harvey. He was also a died-in-the-wool businessman, endowed with that deep instinct, that gift, that knack for buying cheap and selling dear, that shrewdness, limited and petty, that was so characteristic of the Indian business class. He was, however, fascinated by the white woman. I, like all my Market contemporaries, shared his fascination.

The Market was a place of privilege where fugitive and fleeting contact with the white woman was sometimes just possible. How badly in our sex-saturated minds and in our Hollywood-heavy imaginations our Indian women compared with them, for they were better built, better dressed and better groomed; besides, their hair and eyes were more varied and they were, because of their suggestive clothes, infinitely more sensual and also, alas! infinitely more remote.

I was eight when I heard of Seretse Khama and Ruth Williams. News of their marriage was featured in newspapers, on the radio and in the conversation of grown-ups. To me it was something in the realm of a miracle that such a thing could actually happen. I wasn't conscious of it but I was, in some infantile way, in total solidarity with Seretse. Then later, there was the Zulu, Richard Kumalo, who got married to Regina Brooks, a white Orange Free State woman. I remember how it was reported in everyday conversation: "Hey, this Regina Brooks really takes the cake. You know what she told the white cops? She wants to go and live with her husband, even if it means being classified as an African. Can you beat that? The laanie wants to go and live in Orlando township!" And she did and all.

Then, there was this guy Singh who lived a few blocks away from 226, next to the vacant plot where Bangat got buggered up. I don't know what this Singh did — I think, he was an insurance salesman — but in the Location he was a nonentity. Then, like a bolt from the blue, we heard that he and a *laanie cherrie* had been arrested under the Immorality Act. He eventually got married to this sweet Afrikaner girl

116

who worked in the passport office. Boy, was that news sensational. For weeks I, and everybody else in the Location, followed the reports of their plight in the *Pretoria News*, until one day the Government allowed them to go to neighbouring Moçambique.

But Seretse, Kumalo and Singh were all exceptions; nobody else ever got close enough to even touch a white woman, never mind get to know one, love one or marry one.

* * *

This young superb white woman appeared, carrying a medium-sized basket containing three avocado pears. I see her now: blond-haired, leggy with long but well shaped toes in open leather sandals. She was lightly made up and wore a loose fitting white dress and the straps of her garment exposed her freckled shoulders. She radiated sensuality and reminded me of the American actress, Carol Lynley, and yet there was something about her that suggested she was an Afrikaner.

It was a typical summer afternoon, between two and four o'clock when the Market slowed down almost to a snooze. She moved daintily, her feet touched the cement surface lightly and silently. The afternoon was perfect. The evening's rain and the little pools of water along the gutters on the side of the lane, which made the mornings uncomfortable, were now gone.

The woman, like all customers, moved along the lane casually inspecting the produce offered by the different brick and cement stalls. On both sides, a rich variety of fruit and vegetables exposed on the ground and on the racks (made up with the unopened boxes that contained the fruit) drew her attention, beckoned her.

Fara spotted her. He had been talking to Boya and myself, instructing us on how he groomed his hair. He stepped back, turned and exclaimed: "Watch this, guys!" He closed up behind her, overtook her and then, with a desultory air, kept a few paces in front of her. She, with her mind engaged elsewhere, did not notice him. Suddenly he stopped and, then, simulating the action of someone who has suddenly discovered that one of his shoe laces has come loose, bent down.

117

My mother with her granddaughter in 1963.

My family in 1950. I am the one with the bowtie.

The eleven that beat Rangers. Dickie is in the back row, second from left; Satha is fourth from left and I am fifth. Veegee is seated second from left.

226 Jerusalem Street in 1963.

Auntie Jaytoon's house in the Corner.

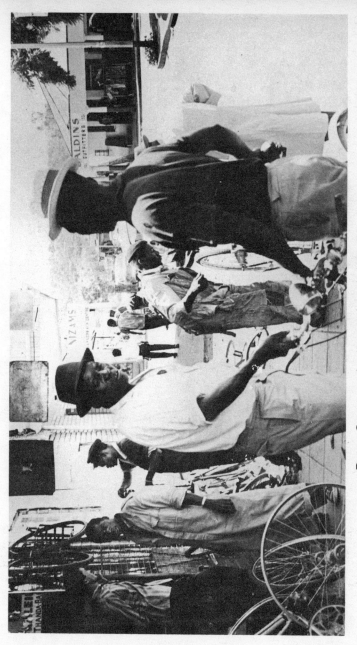

Boom Street — the Location's main street, 1963.

Blood Street. The tall tree in the background was just opposite our house.

Veegee and I on the football ground. Veegee is the short guy in the under-sixteen Arsenal jersey.

The woman, as unmindful as ever, walked slap-bang into him.

The white female body, perfumed and soft, enveloped him. He felt her hands on his back; for to stop her fall she stretched them out. The accident surprised her. That reserve that the whites have towards non-whites was momentarily lost. She was bashful. She apologized. She started to place her hand on the zone where she made contact with him, as if touching the spot would ease or mitigate the supposed pain. She faltered but regained her composure. She checked her hand; the touch did not materialize; but she was still apologetic, and embarrassed that she has allowed the enticement of green groceries to dissipate her attention.

She smiled and said, "Oh, I'm so sorry. I should have paid more mind to what I was doing. Are you all right?"

She wasn't an Afrikaner after all. She must have beeen one of those whites who lived near the Berea Park ground; they were all English-speaking out there.

Fara was as amiable as a sheik. He pooh-poohed the accident away. He enjoyed the proximity of her company. He looked into her fresh pretty face and, without the woman being aware of it, flirted with her.

* * *

One late winter morning I was visited by two burly white men. I eyed them coming up the lane. They weren't customers — I could see by the way they were reading the stall numbers. They passed numbers forty-eight and forty-nine and then stopped in front of the stall. They came up to me and, with a bluntness that was habitual, asked: "Is jou naam Naidoo?" What was this all about, I wondered, but I could see no reason for apprehension; so I said, trying to sound unruffled, "Yes."

Their faces were pumpkin-like, their *platteland* characteristics were unmistakable: glad-neck shirts, shorts, snub-nosed shoes with thick serrated rubber soles; and, clinging to the calves of their rugby legs, grey hoses, under the elastic top of which one of them sported a comb.

Someone repeated the question. I repeated my answer.

One of them took out a notebook and checked my address. Being satisfied, they requested me to accompany them. It was a request but their tone suggested I had no choice. I asked them, more for form than for temerity, why. One of them said, with total indifference, that I was wanted for an identification check: some stolen goods were sold to a secondhand shop in Proes Street. I thought, if I had sold stolen goods to a white shopkeeper, I would hardly have given my real name and address: so I told myself it must be just a formality. They, by retracing their steps, indicated that I had to hurry up. The intimidation of their action goaded me into obedience: I followed.

They stopped when they reached a grey beetle Volkswagen. The novelty of going for a ride in a German-made car (they were just making their appearance in the country then) made me relax a little. The car, however, wasn't empty. Two other rugby players occupied the front seats. How, I asked myself, was I going to fit in among the four heavy weights. In the end, I was squeezed on to the back seat. I found myself sandwiched between the two who had come to collect me.

The car still had the scent of newness but this was mixed with the after odour of beer, tobacco and scrambled eggs. The unprecedented proximity with white bodies made me feel uneasy. I sensed the irony of the situation: anywhere else, and under any other circumstance, such contact would have been *verboten* and considered either illegal or unsocial.

The engine started and the driver was just about to pull away when my uncle Soobree (by marriage to one of my many paternal aunties) appeared. Uncle Soobree worked for my father. He addressed them in that exaggerated and obsequious way so characteristic of the petty Indian trader; and yet I was surprised to find that the tone, not the words, were mixed with an element of dignified self-respect. Why were they taking me? Where were they taking me? The white men assured him in an offhand and summary way that there was nothing to worry about. They were just carrying out a routine identification.

Once we had left the Market, one of them turned to me and said (in Afrikaans): "It's always the same with you

119

Coolies: impossible to pick one of you up without having the entire family troop down to the police station. Eh Naidoo, isn't that so?"

I replied with a forced smile, which the policeman took to mean agreement.

There was truth in what he said. The solidarity of the Location Indians was phenomenal. But his words also implied that the Indians always tried to influence the authorities, always tried to bend the law. The business part of the Indian community did wheel and deal with the all-white bureaucracy as they sometimes did with their customers. It was current that nothing official could be had without an unofficial gift. The word bribe was never used: "Naw, you know how these laanies are? You give them something and you get the thing done without trouble. Ah, I mean, it doesn't cost much: a box of apples, a tray of grapes, a bottle of brandy. What the hell man, if this can expedite matters, heh?"

Yet it wasn't the observation of Indian clannishness, or the tendency of the Indians to bakshish the white administration, that struck me, it was the word 'Coolie', and the careless and cock-sure way it was used.

I knew, ever since I could remember, that it was the white term of abuse for us Indians, but the word, frankly, puzzled and intrigued me. I had often heard my mother use it. The first time I was struck by her use of it was when Ruby came back from Auntie Miriam's, the Malay dressmaker's place, with her new yellow dress. My mother asked her (in Tamil) how much *Coolie pannaw* did Auntie Miriam want for the dress. I knew *pannaw* was money. So I concluded she was asking my sister how much Auntie Miriam wanted for making the dress. *Coolie pannaw*, I figured, meant labour money, but why, I wondered, did the whites apply this Tamil word, *Coolie*, to us and why was it an insult.

The identification was a formality. The white shopkeeper, an old, cigar-smoking Jew, took one look at me and said, shaking his head as he did so, "No, no, it's not him!"

* * *

She was a brunette and she must have been in her early thirties. The Transvaal sunlight had pinched her complexion and made it a little red; she was well groomed and her clothes, and the way she wore them, were patently different from those of the Pretoria white women. She couldn't, however, and this was the outstanding thing about her, speak a word of English or Afrikaans.

Ever since I had seen the Tony Curtis film, *The Perfect Furlough* I couldn't get Paris and France out of my mind. I remembered how Tony Curtis, although he spoke no more than a few words of French, fell in love with a French woman; and he kept singing this song:

If you wanna be famous
It's really up to you.
No matter what you do,
If you wanna be famous
It's really up to you!

And now here was a genuine French woman. I must thank my father. He did the buying that day; he bought a stack of splendid tomatoes. They were big, firm and ripe to perfection. On Saturdays some of the fruit and vegetables were sold loose; that is, in retail quantities, but these tomatoes were sold only in eighteen-pound boxes or nine-pound half boxes. I removed the two broad thin planks from the top of one of the boxes and did the same with the three other boxes I had selected. I then displayed them in pairs, two on top, two below at a forty-five degree angle. This provided the alluring sight of a large rectangle of rubies set in a quadrangle of pine. Fruit in top condition, and just a few hours before being perfectly ripe, have a straight and simple beauty. Pawpaws are a joy of form and tint; an export tray of Cape grapes (containing either the white Waltham Cross or the red Barlinka) is a perfection of shape, scent and hue; a box of Golden Delicious is a celebration of colour and taste — but, on this particular morning, it was these tomatoes which were supreme and which caught the eye of this French woman.

I managed to understand that she wanted some tomatoes and that she wanted to buy them loose. It took me a little while to make her understand that these particular tomatoes were sold only in boxes or in half boxes. I persuaded her finally to buy half a box by taking the tomatoes out and weighing them in front of her. She saw for herself that each and every tomato was perfect and she understood the advantage of buying the lot. She accepted the sale and bought some peas and potatoes as well.

Something else made her outstanding: when she spoke to me, she stood right up to me , looked into my face and peered into my eyes. I swear, it was the first time, the very first time, that a white woman approached me, talked to me, looked at me and listened to me in quite that way. It was, as if I was a fellow being and not a thing of fear and an alien thing of contempt.

She had a few parcels and all the stuff I had sold her. It was obvious she wouldn't have been able to carry everything back to her car. I could see she was ignorant of the "carry boys", those frail juvenile Africans who offered the whites porterage for a pittance; so I made her understand that I would help her. She was visibly pleased. But just before we set off she asked me something. No matter how I tried it was impossible to understand what she was getting at. She betrayed friendly impatience and then she did something that made my heart skip a beat. She reached for my left hand, grasped it firmly at the wrist, turned it slightly towards her and brought it up towards her face and looked at my wrist watch — I wore my watch (Location style) under my wrist, face downward. She held my hand like that while she read the time. The action, which seemed to last more than a moment, was spontaneous, natural and as un-South African as Ruth Williams. Her hand was warm and soft, and her nails were varnished with that bright red polish which, for me, was the very symbol of the female European.

I can't remember what sort of car she had. She wanted to thank me. I would have refused a tip, if she had volunteered it — I wasn't, after all, a "carry boy". She closed the boot and moved off smoothly to the front of the car. She searched

122

for something next to the driver's seat, found it and then extended it to me, she said: "Tenez, c'est pour vous!" I didn't of course understand what the words meant but I realized she was offering me a little creamed pastry. I told myself: Hey Jay, imagine this white woman is giving you a pastry. I knew (because of the songs of Harry Belafonte and Nat king Cole) the French words *merci* and *beaucoup;* so I used these to thank her. She was tickled pink. She bid me farewell by shaking my hand. At that moment, I was convinced, that the whites of Europe were definitely different from the whites in Pretoria or South Africa. The longing to quit the country and to go to Europe certainly took root then.

19

There was something peculiar about Bhiraj that evening. That look of martyrdom that he was wont to wear on his face and bear on his shoulders was absent and replaced by a self-satisfaction and a huge confident smile. I eyed him and sensed that he had something up his sleeve. "What's up? You've got a girl friend or something? A new job?"

He shook his head and, with his eyes twinkling and his voice heavy with the tone of largesse, he said, "Do you want a pair of McGregor socks?"

The question surprised me but I played ball: "Well, I won't say no to American socks!" He smartly took off his pair of brogue shoes, removed his socks and then, removed a second pair: they were brand-new.

"Here!" He handed me the socks and added: "I'm sorry I've had to wear them a little but my feet are clean."

* * *

When the 1958 season came to an end, Swaraj had defeated Rangers once again and had even gone on to defeat Delfos, the other outstanding Pretoria team. I played on both occasions, but against Delfos I had an off day. It's impossible to explain why this was so, but there are days when, no matter what you do, nothing seems to come right: my stops, my passes, my tackles and my dribbles all seemed to go awry. Still near the dying minutes of the match — the score was two all — I started the move that brought on the winning goal. Swaraj triumphed but it certainly wasn't a happy day for me.

After that match we were effectively the best team in the

Location but our triumph came too late: we had missed the league competition. Rangers got promoted to the all-important and prestigious Transvaal League. Our two great rivals (and now inferiors) played in the super competition while we were confined to the ordinary Pretoria League. The result was frustration and boredom. No local team could compete with us; so we entered a round of no-contest matches. Worse still, we were forced to appear in many curtain-raisers for Transvaal League matches, where Delfos or Rangers played against the celebrated teams of Johannesburg, Germiston and Benoni.

The prestige of Swaraj nevertheless drew a lot of new and young players to the team. And now that matches weren't so crucial it became possible, now and then, to experiment with an untried player. This is how Bhiraj Nana entered Swaraj.

I was in standard seven when I was appointed captain of the first School side. I was seventeen then. One of the players making up the School eleven was Bhiraj. He played, as I did, in the forward line. But he was more of a goal-scorer than I was. I knew that when I used to play for Arsenal, he used to play for our old rivals, All Bharats. He started appearing at the Corner and slowly became part of the clan made up of Innie, Veegee, Butcher and myself. Later he came up to 226, sat in my room with the others and listened to LPs.

I heard that he slept on the kitchen floor in his parents' two-roomed rented house. Ranga had married, had a double bed and a room of his own; so his single bed at the opposite end of mine was free. I asked my mother if Bhiraj could come and sleep at 226. She consented without hesitation. When I suggested the idea to Bhiraj, he was surprised and then delighted. From that day he became a kind of second brother.

There were those who said we resembled each other. It's true that we did, at a glance, look alike, but his shoulders were rounded, his chest was pigeon-shaped, his hair was thicker and straighter, his hips and thighs were ampler and he was slightly taller.

Anyway, he signed up for Swaraj. Not long thereafter he was given a chance to play. The red, white and green colours

125

of Swaraj suited him. It made him look virile and handsome. I remember that particular day. The sun hung in a cloudless blue sky, bleaching the white shorts and drying up the semi-green grass; and I recall how superb he looked when, just before the kick off, he took his place on the field. And yet his performance though not a washout was a disappointment. He was dropped for the next match.

He urged me to appeal to Dickie, and to some of the other selectors, to give him another chance. I told Dickie that one match wasn't enough to judge a player's real worth. Fair's fair. Bhiraj got a second chance but his showing was once again disappointing. I remember, at one moment, I lobbed him a properly weighted through pass, as I had done on so many occasions for Veegee — we were playing against Pirates and their defence was anything but compliant — and the ball, as intended, landed just a few yards ahead of Bhiraj. He was a strong runner. I got off the mark faster than he did but over a hundred-yard stretch he always beat me to the finishing line. Now, I saw him picking up speed and gathering pace.

Coming in to challenge him was Pittacauli, a short stocky fellow from Brits. He was one of those many more-brawn-than-brain players that characterized the Pirates side. When he charged, you'd swear, if you closed your eyes and opened your ears, that a bull was stampeding towards you. He wore a handkerchief like a bandage round his head; this made him seem even more seismic. For some reason Dickie called him When-The-Sun-Sets.

Bhiraj saw When-The-Sun-Sets closing in. Veegee and I had, more than once, faced similar challenges. The trick was to get to the ball first, and to avoid his boots and body with a lot of speed, some anticipation and a little pluck. It was seemingly dangerous but effectively a fairly easy thing to do. Bhiraj's speed slackened. The closer he got to the Pirates' player, the slower his run became: he failed to reach the ball.

Hell man, I told myself, this bloody guy is scared. But I had a re-think and after a little while I convinced myself that perhaps my pass was, after all, a little too heavy. Later I executed a similar pass and the result was exactly the same.

Bhiraj had the speed and the shot but not the nerve or the confidence — it was impossible to conclude otherwise — to be a real footballer. As was to be expected, he was dropped for the next match. I think Dickie, though he kept silent about it, shared my opinion and had detected (possibly earlier than I had) the absence of guts in Bhiraj's play; for when I appealed to him to give Bhiraj another chance, he turned a deaf ear.

Bhiraj, however, took Dickie and the other selectors' reluctance to pick him as a manifestation of Tamil bias. When, in confidence, I heard him utter this charge, I was dumbstruck. I must have betrayed some of my astonishment; for he fixed me with an injured look and said, "Ja, you don't know about these things. You don't see the differences. You accept everybody. These guys in the Corner stick together. With them it's Tamils first — to them I'm just a Bun, that's why they don't want to pick me."

This unexpected lament almost broke his voice. I felt uncomfortable and hopeless. I said nothing but reflected: maybe among the selectors there might just have been this bias but when I thought of my uncle Anand and Bathos, I knew it could not be. As for Dickie, he was too much of a connoisseur to let a little thing like Bhiraj's being a Gujarati hinder his appreciation of a real footballer. The clannishness of the Location — the fact that Tamils married Tamils, Calcuttias Calcuttias, Malays Malays, Koknies Koknies, Khojas Khojas, Memons Memons, Hindu Gujaratis Hindu Gujaratis and Muslim Gujaratis Muslim Gujaratis — was absurd and regrettable. The whites set up barriers but we, in our own petty way, set up barriers as well. But I knew it was the rigidities and fantasies of the Motherland; the fripperies of language, religion and ritual, the old India again.

But football wasn't Indian. The venerable Swaraj team stood above linguistic and religious differences. I knew from discussions at the Corner that Gona, Nades and Dickie championed a non-racial football organisation. I had heard them talk enthusiastically of a single "Coloured", African and Indian league. Bhiraj's charge was without foundation; besides, I had seen his performance, I had observed it from

127

close up — on the football field you didn't have to commit suicide but you had to have a certain amount of guts. Of course, I didn't tell him this, but the projection of his own weakness on to others disappointed me.

Bhiraj, after school, worked for Baniyans, the outfitters' shop at the corner of Boom and Fourth Streets. When he finished standard eight (he was a year ahead of me) he left school and worked full time for Baniyan's. We continued to have our breakfast together like we used to do when we were both still at school. After work he came to 226 and had a wash before going down to his parents' place where he had his evening meals. Sometimes I was on hand to greet him and to exchange snippets of news.

* * *

That socks gift was only the beginning; later he would offer me a tie, a leather belt or a handkerchief. I didn't protest; I didn't think of them as theft; I accepted them as a token of friendship. Besides, I was aware that working for an Indian boss was hardly a boon: in general, they under-paid, insisted on long, unregulated hours, provided no holidays and no compensation for accident or sickness and none for dismissal.

One day, about six months later, Bhiraj made me a new offer. "Jay, I can get you a pair of Jarman shoes for one third or one quarter of the actual price!" He gave me that twinkling smile again.

"What do you mean?"

"Well, is there a Jarman shoes that you'd really like to have?"

I recalled at that time that there was a pair of blue suede shoes that I had noticed once in the window of Baniyan's. Normally, I wouldn't have been attracted to them. They seemed to be the kind of things that the white ducktails of Hillbrow would wear, but Carl Perkins gave them another symbol and a different prestige.

"Well, I must admit, I wouldn't mind having that pair of blue suede, Jarman shoes."

"You know, it's not a moccasin?"

128

"Yes, I know."

"OK, the shoe is marked £3 7/6. If you really want it, I'll get it for £1."

Delighted and intrigued, I asked him, how that was possible.

"Well you see we have a lot of Africans who come to the shop. Now, you know, that these poor guys can't buy what they want just like that. Think now that they're going to buy those Jarman shoes. They first lay down a deposit — they might pay 10/-, £1 or £1 7/6. Then they'll come back every week, most of the time, and pay a little more money. Then finally they'll come and make the last payment and then take the shoes."

"Yes, but I don't see how that makes me get the shoes as cheap as you say."

"You'll see, it's quite simple. First, I make up a dud receipt with a dud deposit; and then a week later, I make an entry on the same receipt for another dud payment, and so on until it's time to pay just £1 to have the shoes."

I looked at him straight in the eye and made him understand, without uttering a word, that he wasn't going to get me into the shop even if it meant getting the shoes for nothing.

He smiled again, confidently. "Naw, don't worry, all you have to do is to get one of the boys working for your toppie to come to the shop — to come and see me with the receipt and the outstanding amount in cash. There is no risk whatsoever; but the buyer has to be an African because the name on the receipt will be an African's name. What do you say?"

"You're sure it'll work?"

"Don't worry, it's a cinch — I'm telling you, it's above suspicion."

Bhiraj was right; it was above suspicion.

After that he became ruthlessly ambitious: he got himself an experienced partner, an African chap. I don't know how he worked it, but he really set about his task coldly and methodically. One day he came carrying two brand-new suitcases — they were empty. He asked me (for the sake of form) if he could leave them on the top of my wardrobe. Then he regularly began to fill them up with brand new shirts, jerseys, socks, trousers and raincoats.

* * *

One winter evening he invited me to accompany him to his associate and accomplice, Fatty. Fatty lived in Boom Street, in a small room at the back of Master's butcher's shop. Fatty, as well as being fat, was very black. He had a huge winning smile and was, if you took away the fat, quite handsome. That evening he was smartly dressed: Flosheim shoes, a pair of gabardine trousers, a Jayson leather belt, an Arrow floral shirt and a McGregor woolen slipover. From his speech, tone and general manner it was evident that he was one of those smooth-talking smart ones, a *cleva*, a sophisticated *tsotsi*. I detected a mocking wily glint in his eyes. Two young buxom African girls lounged on his bed. The room was dim, crowded and stuffy with the odour of Vaseline and unwashed bed clothes. Kwela music — the unmistakable sound of Spokes Mashiyane's penny whistle — came, clear and soft, from an unsighted record player.

"Well this is Fatty! Fatty, this is my best friend, Jay." We shook hands. His hands were soft and his finger nails were clean and long.

"Fatty, show Jay your rod!"

"Sure."

Fatty went to a dark brown twill overcoat hanging behind the badly painted wooden door, searched the inside pocket and took out a Barretta automatic pistol. It was the first time I had seen a real pistol. Fatty handed the gun to me and said: "Here feel it!"

I looked at him, surprised by the invitation. I must have betrayed anxiety; for Fatty, in a reassuring and slightly patronising tone, said: "Oh, don't worry, it's not loaded!"

When the gun was nice and snug in my hand, I was surprised to find how strong and confident I suddenly felt. Fatty looked at me and said, in a throw-away tone, "I can get you a rod, if you want."

"Well, I wouldn't mind having something like this Barretta — although something a little smaller would be even better."

130

He smiled and said in easy fashion, 'I'll see what I can do."

Fatty, after that evening, came to 226 once every fortnight. He always came after dark, and always with a large strap-handled leather bag. When he came, I greeted him and then led him to my room and to Bhiraj. I never found out what the precise arrangement or deal between them was; I always left them to conduct their business on their own. I did however notice, from the way Fatty carried the bag, that it was empty when he came but full when he left.

* * *

Bhiraj never talked to me about his business with Fatty. Ever since that day he accused Dickie and the others of being Tamil chauvinists a certain reserve had entered our relationship. It was his habit to come to 226 after work, to wash, to go to visit his mother and thereafter either to come to the Corner or to return to my room, but now in the evenings he disappeared and only came to 226 to sleep.

Then one day, when I came back late in the afternoon from the Empire — I'd just seen Kirk Douglas in *Spartacus* — I noticed Ambi, impatiently waiting at the yard gate. When I got to her, she blurted out: "Hey Jay, Bhiraj is at the police station!"

"What? What did you say?"

"Bhiraj has been arrested. He sent someone here, nè. He said you must hide his things. But I knew you weren't here; so I took his two bags and gave it to Maloo at the back."

Maloo was the Muslim neighbour directly behind 226. I knew she was reliable. I was delighted with Ambi's quick thinking but the news of Bhiraj's arrest left me cold and numb.

Fortunately Bhiraj was detained for only a day or two. The Baniyan brothers dropped their charges. Bhiraj's family vowed that their son, to make up for the losses he had caused, would work for the Outfitters' without payment, and for an agreed period. Being businessmen, they quickly saw the advantage between prison and unpaid employment.

Bhiraj never returned to 226. I met him on two occasions

131

but these meetings were strained. On both occasions he was with fellow Gujaratis. His maverick, un-Gujarati behaviour must have troubled his family and relatives and, knowing the Location mentality, must have persuaded them that the cause of his delinquency lay in his relations with Swaraj, the Corner and perhaps even 226.

A few months later Ebies and I were walking down Von Wielligh Street. It was the routine during the eleven o'clock school break for the two of us to go off and buy ourselves hamburgers from Parsons, a white café nearby. We were puzzled to see Bhiraj approaching us from the post office side of Von Wielligh Street.

"Hi Bhiraj," I said.

Ebies greeted him with a, "Hi Bhij!"

"Hi guys!"

Bhiraj looked at me; I could see he was feeling proud and excited.

"Hey Jay, I'm leaving for Southern Rhodesia. I got an uncle there. I'm going to stay with him for two weeks and then I'm flying off to London."

"London! Hey, that's great news."

Ebies, with ebullience, said, "Hey, you lucky bastard, you're going to Laanie-land, it's great, man!"

"Well, Bhiraj I wish you luck," I said.

Ebies tapped him on the shoulder, and said, "Take care!"

We shook hands and he left. It was an incredibly brief farewell. I felt that we had things to say to each other, yet neither he nor I knew how to express them or even how to begin to express them. I felt a heavy sensation of disappointment, of something that ought to have been said and wasn't. I should have hugged him; maybe I should even have shed a tear or two but I suppressed all emotion and displayed a faked detachment.

20

"Old Block" was a remote figure. Every Saturday for seven years when I was a boy, he woke me, prepared my breakfast and drove me to the Market. In the mornings he approached the window of my bedroom (this is when I occupied the spare room that gave on to the yard) and roused me out of bed by calling out once, and once only, "Jay!" Thereafter I dressed, washed, entered the old kitchen and found, waiting for me on the table, a cup of coffee and two slices of buttered toast. I ate alone.

After breakfast I left the house and went out to the 1954, navy blue Dodge truck parked outside (later it would be the 1957 two-tone, red and grey Plymouth car) and waited. Presently he joined me and we would set off. The familiar sights of the "Coloured" sections of the Location in Jerusalem and Struben Streets came in view. Then we entered the white area. First, the poor white area of Potgieter Street and then Prinsloo Street — the Street with rich and gaudy Indian shops — and finally the Market where the Location, like an oversight, recreated itself in the form of staid stalls.

Throughout the three-mile journey no words were exchanged. In winter the silence was occasionally broken:

Father: "Are you chaps playing tomorrow?"

Me: "Yes, we're playing against Pretorians (or whatever team it might have been)."

Father: "What time does the match start?"

Me: "Two o'clock; we're the curtain raiser" (or sometimes, I would answer: "Quarter to four. We're the main match").

Once my father gently reproached me for not having informed him that I was playing in a friendly match on a Wednesday afternoon. I hardly suspected that such an unofficial match, where the sides did not even have jerseys, would interest him.

"Old Block's" boyhood was steeped in back-breaking work. He was a taciturn man, moody, hot-tempered and tough. He went to bed early, got up early and swore by the belief that the early bird catches the worm. Neatness, cleanliness and punctuality seemed second nature to him. One day he told me, because I had been late, "You'll be late for your own funeral." He was also a good cook. Every Sunday he carefully prepared boiled food, which the rest of the family regarded (in contrast to the mutton and chicken curry mother prepared) as European fare.

As for the other days of the week, from Monday to Friday, I just caught a glimpse of him, that is, if I got up early enough. He came home from the Market after midday, then after his meal he would retire for an afternoon nap, then he got up and left, returning again in the evening for supper. By eight p.m. his day was done. Everybody in the house knew he had gone to bed, although no "good nights" were ever exchanged.

* * *

I must admit that father of mine puzzled me; he was so rarely at home and, yet his presence was always felt and his authority always feared. I remember wondering how this man, so grave in countenance and so brooding in temperament, had begot me. He seemed quite remote from the passion and tenderness of the sexual act. There were moments when he was less patriarchal, when he was actually benign and amiable. Round-faced and clean-shaven, his features somehow matched his stocky figure. He was not a tall man, but he was tall enough to make a worth-while goalkeeper.

His lack of schooling may have been the cause of his shyness and his seclusion; and may also have been the reason for his evident reluctance to engage in talk. He rarely spoke to us. When he did it was nearly always for a formal or practical end, like asking about the health of someone who had recently been ill or sending someone on an errand.

134

I was aware that a wise man was not necessarily an edu-
cated man but, I couldn't help thinking that an ability to
read and a capacity to write would have made him, not a
wiser man — for wise men are rare — but, perhaps, a better
man; certainly a different man.

He never talked about his lack of education but later in life
I had occasion to observe his sense of inferiority and the dis-
advantage he suffered for having been without it. Indres, the
smart alecky son of Mr Pather, came to Pretoria for two
weeks. One day, with the *Rand Daily Mail* in his hand, he
went up to my father and, pointing to the lines of some article, said, "Uncle! Uncle, just look at this!" My father feigned
interest and shook his head, as if to say: Yes, quite extraordi-
nary. I pretended not to notice.

Still, a lack of education did not prevent him from being
extremely dignified in manner. I didn't know if he was
taught directly by a puritan and upright father or by plain
common-sense observation (I asked him once who had
taught him to cook; he replied: "I see and I do"), but I did
know he had habits and qualities which made him stand out
from the other fathers of the Location. For one thing he was,
apart from general cleanliness, mindful of his appearance: he
brushed and polished his shoes daily; dressed neatly, chose
his clothes with discretion and combined their colours with
a severe but natural good taste. His body movements were
sedate and absent of all clumsiness, and his manner of walking was regular like a soldier's and quiet like a cat's. He was
also special because he was, contrary to Location tradition,
an unwavering tee-totaler.

So upright, quiet and domestic was he that I completely
refused to believe a story about him being a keen billiards
player. It was one my mother recounted; I suspect she did so
in order to subvert the idealized and conventional view I had
of him. My mother's revelation jolted me because I had somehow learnt to associate billiard rooms with Rah's, Mooloo's
and Sooboo's, the cafés of the Location, which tended to be
(or were thought to be) the lairs of petty gangsters, layabouts
and gamblers. Billiard rooms, I was convinced, were places
good folk shunned. So I was prompted into the rare action of

going up to him and asking him candidly to disprove my mother. His face, upon hearing my request, lit up with a large and unusual smile. But his reticence ran true to form: he said nothing to contradict my mother's story and nothing to confirm it.

"He's independent," it was said of him. It must have been true, for he had a single friend, Mr Tebba, who was a few years younger than he was. My father didn't go out much. I remember the two occasions, the two afternoons, he deigned to go to the cinema. He went to the Empire at the urging of Mr Tebba to see Richard Widmark in *Street with No Name* and to the Orient at my mother's urging to see Raj Kapoor in *Awara*.

He never went to the Temple. His whole way of life suggested he was indifferent to religion; he certainly displayed no superstition. Yet, sickness — or fear of worse — made him turn, in a half-hearted way, to faith-healing. He went to Germiston (the town where my mother was born). A woman there caught the *marrill* and could, it was claimed, cure the sick. There was on that day a motley crowd of credulous Tamil men, women and children, toing and froing, eager and anxious to witness a miracle. During the excitement someone stepped on his foot. He came back as tired as ever and footsore as well.

One of his sisters, as uneducated as he was and more limited in experience, bathed his foot in overheated water. She can, to a certain extent, be forgiven; for the idea of measuring the temperature of the water with a thermometer was foreign to the Location and outside the compass of her mind. The bruise on his foot became a burn, the burn became a sore and the sore, in time, became an infection. Dr Ronnie, Location-born but London-educated and newly qualified, examined and treated him. Later, Dr Kaplan, the old standby white doctor, examined and treated him as well but to no avail: the infection spread.

* * *

Three weeks after the Germiston visit, on a dull cold winter

136

afternoon, Ranga and I bumped into Mr Tebba as he was leaving the house.

"Hello, Mr Tebba,"I said.

Mr Tebba's moustache, his full regular teeth and his large head reminded me of Clark Gable. But his normally jovial and playful smile was that afternoon put into quarantine.

"Hey, have you fellas seen your father?"

"No," we sheepishly admitted. We had deliberately stayed away from our father's bedroom. We were not used to him being sick and we felt awkward and embarrassed about visiting him. Of course, I had noticed the doctors, the relatives and the friends who never ceased coming. And I had noticed the anxiousness written on mother's worn and tired face, but I convinced myself that it was these Indians again making a mountain out of a molehill. But Mr Tebba's implied reproach was disturbing.

A week later Dr Poollye, the best of the Location's doctors, realized that "Old Block" was suffering from sugar diabetes. But by then it was too late: gangrene had already set in. He was taken to the hospital and his right leg was amputated but he died a day later, victim of a post-operation stroke.

I learnt that he was fifty-six years old. I was nineteen then and fifty-six struck me as being a fair old innings. What appalled me though was the realization that it only took four weeks and three days for diabetes, superstition, gangrene and amputation to mischieve his end.

* * *

It was a glorious day, just about twilight, when I learnt that "Old Block" was dead. Ranga and I waited outside the house, next to the iron railings of the garden fence. Our uncles and aunts drifted towards the house and, as they passed us, acknowledged their sympathies with a discreet tilt of the head. Our friends soon appeared. I couldn't help thinking that they, in extending their sympathies to us, imitated their elders and that we, in accepting them, were imitating ours. "Please accept my sincere regrets," Innie said, with a voice unusually grave and with an expression unusually solemn.

137

We exchanged a stilted handshake. Satchoo, Dickie, Veegee, Butcher and others imitated Innie. The whole proceeding struck me as so much play acting — I had to suppress a growing desire to laugh.

Somehow the death in the family didn't seem to register. "Old Block's" body was still at the hospital. Nothing, save the loud wailing of mother and the softer wailings of my many aunts, suggested that something untoward had happened. Of course, there were lots of people milling around the house but lots of people milled around the house when Ranga got married, and when Swaraj won the Transvaal League cup, father invited the team to the house for a tea and cake banquet. The atmosphere now, of course, was sombre and the very opposite of jubilation; but an hour or two later, I heard the sound of laughter coming from the kitchen.

* * *

A few days before my father died I was with my mother in that hospital room of his. He implored her, "Don't you think I'll be better off at home? The food here is terrible." His eyes, I noticed with discomfort, were crowded with tears. I saw my mother, for the very first time, touch his hand, discreetly, ever so discreetly. My presence was momentarily ignored. The door was slightly ajar and from outside the bustling sound of the visitors rudely contrasted with the tense forlorn atmosphere within the room. My father was usually clean shaven but that day bristles covered his face. Their greyness surprised me. The four weeks at home and the two days in hospital had aged him. It was almost as if weeks had turned into years and days had turned into months. I was taken aback by the visible deterioration and yet, in an odd, indeterminate way, he seemed to have grown friendlier, gentler and less remote.

I slipped out of the room and savoured the familiar atmosphere — it was like seeing an old friend again. I walked down the green well-polished floor, down the long corridor and past an African nurse with her starched white uniform, which was almost as white as her teeth and almost as creaseless as her complexion; and then to the entrance hall, which was annexed to the casualty ward. I stepped outside. The particular odour of the hospital, even there, clung to the air. I saw a few white doctors, some ambulance men and a policeman. A group of "Coloured" visitors stood around chatting. It looked, as if they were talking about football. A number of Africans paced the court yard. Some were evidently employed in the hospital, others were visitors and most looked like visit-less patients trying to achieve vicarious comfort by being in the proximity of the visitors coming and going. There were also a few Indians, anxious not to be late, scurrying up the gradient tarmac. I thought of my father and wondered how a proud, independent man, such as he was, would cope with a single leg. I found no answer. I looked up at the blue sky, sensed the presence of the bare trees and, suddenly, felt like praying.

* * *

The body arrived early the next morning. By midday, "Old Block" had been washed and shaved, and dressed in a sober brown suit. I wondered about the fact that the women folk had washed him. Did they see him in the nude? Did they touch and rub him all over? I couldn't bring myself to imagine it. I didn't dare ask my mother but the thought left me bewildered and convinced me that adult conduct was indeed strange and beyond comprehension.

"Old Block"'s death emphasized my youth; for being the youngest male member of the family, I was commissioned by tradition to perform the funeral rites. There were many things to do although most of them were of the don't variety: Don't eat meat! Don't go to the cinema! Don't listen to records! Don't switch the radio on! Don't play football! Don't hurt yourself! Don't, above all, bleed — not a drop of blood must be shed for the next fifteen days! There was also one do: you must cut all your hair off! I did not for a single instance believe in the credibility of any of these rites. To me they were just a lot of (I remember this word from *The Quiet Man*) shenanigans.

139

On the day of the burial, before the coffin left the house, I had to perform a number of rituals. Khrishnaner, playing now the role of an Indian priest, showed me what I had to do. I was supposed to repeat the ceremonial movements he executed and repeat the mantra he uttered. I found the exercise senseless. Each time I was instructed to do and say something I protested by asking "why." But Khrishnaner ignored my questions and patiently asked me to do as I was bidden.

Every gesture performed had to be executed three times. Sometimes, I repeated the action twice and then asked Khrishnaner if my father would still go to heaven or into higher reincarnation or wherever it was he was supposed to go. My Uncle Rajee, witnessing my protest, became impatient and irritated. "Why don't you go to India and ask them all the questions you want there? Right now, just do what Khrishnaner tells you to do!" Even my friends became impatient. Butcher, in his usual blunt manner, counselled: "Ag, for your father's sake just do what they tell you to do!"

"Old Block" died on Tuesday and was buried on Friday. I wondered about this. Hindus were cremated. Gandhi was cremated. Even General Smuts was cremated. Why wasn't he cremated?

21

I hadn't seen Soobathie since that fateful Tuesday. She was present during those long quiet days that separated the day of dying from the day of burial but there was such a rigid separation of the sexes that I only once or twice caught a glimpse of her.

A few days after the funeral I called at her parents' home. Soobathie's younger sister spotted me before I reached the house; so when I got there, Soobathie was already waiting for me on the stoep. She tried to look sombre and serious but I could see she was happy and excited. We exchanged the usual discreet greetings. She teasingly brushed the top of my head with her hand. "Hey, it's growing quickly, nè?"

I caught her hand and looked into her face. Her clear complexion, her bright eyes and her beckoning lips made me want to kiss her but just then her parents appeared. Their faces, I couldn't help noticing, were flushed with excitement. They became aware of my presence and hastily checked their exuberance — real joy was whizzed away by false solemnity. They enquired formally about the funeral and formally paid their respects; then they scurried away, eager to continue what my presence had obviously interrupted. As soon as they were out of sight, I asked Soobathie what was happening.

"Well, don't you remember Rajas is getting married on Sunday?" No, I didn't remember. I hadn't remembered. I had been so engulfed by the atmosphere of death and so preoccupied by the ceremony of burial that I had forgotten that the world was still turning, that people were still being born and that marriages were still being consummated, that my girl friend's younger sister was on the verge of becoming a wife. The sudden realization that my father's death hardly mat-

141

tered to those who weren't directly affected, disconcerted me.

"Ah, yes. So what's happening?"

"Well, you know, the marriage is at the boy's place — so they're getting ready to go to Benoni."

"Are you going too?"

"Yes, but they're leaving tonight. My brothers and sisters will join them there, early Sunday morning."

I looked at her relieved and pleased.

"Yes, my parents won't be here tomorrow. I'll come and see you in the evening."

Two weeks later the newly weds were at the bride's place. I knew Koopoo, the bridegroom, well; he had been a neighbour in Jerusalem Street.

* * *

Koopoo and Sonny (another Jerusalem Street neighbour) extended an invitation to me: "Do you want to come to the Duikings?"

"Duikings? What's that?"

They both smiled, pleased at having had my anticipated naïveté confirmed.

It was Sonny who asked the question and it was Sonny who spoke: "You don't know what's the Duikings? Well, then, you simply must come along with us."

"What about Tammy?"

"Ag, you can miss Tammy for once in your life. Nobody's going to know. Isn't it Koopoo?"

Koopoo gave a cynical smile and aired a few brief half-hearted assurances. I detected a challenge in his response, as if he was telling Sonny: "Ag, leave this snotnose here and let's high-tail it there on our own!"

After Koopoo's reaction, I felt it was impossible to refuse.

In the rainy season the stream that separated the Location from the white part of Pretoria looked a little like a river. It ran northward beyond the unfenced rugby ground and the fenced off white bus depot where, like a fugitive, it quietly disappeared among the shrubbery and woods. Exactly where it went thereafter the intelligence of the Location didn't know and didn't care.

142

No one possessed a swimming costume — no one thought of possessing one. Koopoo and Sonny stripped without ceremony. I felt shy and awkward at seeing their nakedness so carelessly exposed. Hesitantly and timidly I also undressed. They, claiming that they were swimming, splashed about with bravado. I joined them and did the same but with the caution and clumsiness of a novice.

My little adventure went undiscovered. Weeks later, Vadival, our next door neighbour and self-appointed protector, got to know about it. How? Maybe Koopoo told him. Vadival lectured me in a brotherly fashion: it wasn't staying away from Tamil School that he minded but rather that I had dipped myself into the suspect waters of the River. Vadival, as if he was more than wise to my fear, stressed that the frightening illness Argina, who lived next-door to Lalie's Café, had contracted was due to swimming in the Duikings. Argina, an amiable fellow, had eyes surrounded by sores. I found it difficult, almost unbearable, to look at him. His appearance, especially in a face-to-face situation, sent a tremor through my spine. This tale scared the wits out of me. For days after that I kept a watch for the first signs of Argina's illness.

After several weeks, when I was beginning to forget about Vadival's warning, I heard about what happened to Koopoo. Koopoo, Sonny and Vella (they called Vella, Boerkie because his skin was so fair) were in the pool splashing about when they were caught by a band of "Coloured" ruffians. The three, naked and defenceless in the water, were cursed and hit with stones flung from the bank. The "Coloured" boys even threatened to walk away with all their clothes. Koopoo and the others desperately pleaded and just managed to retrieve two trousers and one vest, but the ruffians, because Koopoo seemed to be the biggest of the three, refused to hand him back his trousers. When Koopoo insisted they slapped and punched him.

When I met Koopoo and asked him if what had happened was true, he, as boastful and as haughty as ever, said: "Do you really think something like that could happen to me? You know me, I'd kill the bastards if they just as much thought of doing something like that to me!"

Later I asked Sonny and Vella about the incident. They confirmed the original account but asked me to keep the story to myself as they didn't want to get into Koopoo's bad books.

Koopoo was one of those who, when he got into a fight, used to run home and call his father. And his father was one of those who acted on the principle that blood is thicker than water. I recollect how his father actually got into a fight with someone else's father one afternoon, because of Koopoo. Such a thing was inconceivable at home. "Old Block's" consign to my mother concerning us was: "They can do what they like outside but I don't want anyone coming to the house with any complaints!"

Koopoo and his parents left Jerusalem Street and Pretoria, and went to live in Benoni, a Reef town about fifty-six miles from Pretoria. The Indian quarter there was smaller, poorer and dirtier than the Location. Koopoo's father hawked fruit and vegetables and used to make his rounds in the white areas in a neat wooden cart drawn by a magnificent chestnut stallion. I wondered if he would, in Benoni, continue hawking; and regretted that I wouldn't be able to see him go by with his impressive horse and carriage.

* * *

Since their departure I hadn't thought, seen or heard of Koopoo. Now, after these many years, I wondered how we would get along. When we did meet in the front room of his in-law's house, I immediately sensed that he had changed very little. His patronising air and the high opinion he held of himself soon wearied me. He and Soobathie's brother got into an intellectual discussion. I was prepared to talk about football and bodybuilding, but anything abstract left me indifferent. So I took advantage of their preoccupation to coax Soobathie out on to the stoep where, in the extreme corner, the obscurity of the night and a little wooden bench provided an ideal petting place.

Two weeks later we met again. Koopoo had come down to Pretoria on his blue Vespa scooter. As on the previous occa-

144

sion he was extravagantly confident and condescending; and even more wearisome was the ostentatious way every member of his wife's family doted on him. I felt particularly neglected. I felt lousy. Why, I asked myself, were they so indifferent to me? Why were they so full of Koopoo this and Koopoo that?

Their attitude was puzzling. I felt that Soobathie and I were as good as married, except, of course, for all the formal stuff that goes with Indian weddings. The difference really beat me and vexed me.

Friday, a week later, Soobathie and I were in the front room. I had come with a couple of hamburgers that I had picked up at Rangana's Café on the corner of Cowie and Grand Streets. She sent one of her small sisters for a couple of Seven Ups. We were just about to have our evening meal when the telephone in the adjoining room rang. Soobathie's mother appeared. She greeted me hastily and asked Soobathie to accompany her to the kitchen. Once again I felt like an outsider. Soobathie was away for some time before returning. The call had come from Benoni. Koopoo, it appeared, had tried to commit suicide. A little later, Soobathie's mother came and urged me to wait with her daughter. She and Soobathie's father, she explained in a hush, were going to Benoni but they wouldn't be staying overnight; so would I wait until they got back.

I consented and was secretly delighted that for once I had been considered part of the family circle, and I was even more delighted that I would have a long night alone with Soobathie.

I wasn't really worried about Koopoo. I thought that his attempt must have been more show than substance, and that anyway it was just like him to want to draw attention to himself by doing something histrionic so late at night.

By ten o'clock Soobathie's younger sisters and brothers were safely asleep. We installed ourselves in the arm-chair — the one in the front room next to the window that had a view on the street. Throughout our wait, which was well beyond midnight, we became as intimate as our clothes would allow. The pleasure I got from the radiance of her

145

smile, the allure of her dark eyes, the neat beauty of her nose and the delight of her body made that night memorably passionate. Yet perhaps because our intimacy was so totally silent; there was something about it that was curiously chaste and ceremonial.

Her parents were back at two in the morning. Koopoo, after quarrelling with his wife, had drunk caustic soda. He was rushed to the local hospital but was still in a coma and still "critical."

I walked home. The night was clear; the absence of the moon made the stars all the more brighter. The streets were deserted and in that quiet and still atmosphere the words of Frankie Lyman's song came to my mind:

Why do fools fall in love?
Why do birds sing so gay?
And lovers await the break of day?
Why do they fall in love?
Why does the rain fall from up above?
Why do fools fall in love?
Why do they fall in love?

I then banished the lyrics and the tune from my mind and wondered about Koopoo's age. He was, I calculated, about five years older than I was. What could have pushed a twenty-four year old, I asked myself, to take such a drastic step. I recalled Butcher's mother. She was in her late thirties when she, too, committed suicide by drinking caustic soda. Then I remembered an American expert on radio one day say that the act of suicide is committed at the precise moment when sanity gives way to insanity. My thoughts returned to Soobathie; I felt warm and elated but Koopoo and his mad act kept breaking into my reverie.

Later in the morning I learnt that Soobathie's sister, after a month or so of marriage, was now a widow and was soon to be a mother.

22

I made new friends that year, the year that my father died. Abdul Sattar Aboobaker and I had been in the same class since standard two and I doubt, for all of that period, if I ever exchanged a single word with him. He was nearly in every way my direct opposite. He was fat and round, and played no sport; he seemed not to be interested in girls and, in the classroom, made no comment and caused no attraction. He was in my eyes, and in those of Patrick and Ebies', a mere sissy, but he didn't on that account draw my dislike or contempt (nor did anyone in the class for that matter). At worst, I was indifferent to him. Now in standard nine, after the second term results were announced, he came to me and invited me to join a study group that met at his place. I found the invitation from someone I had ignored for more than seven years generous and flattering; so I accepted without hesitation.

Thus, every afternoon, after school and after lunch, I went off to 201 Boom Street, where Sattar's father and elder brother ran an outfitters' shop that catered for the African market. At the side of the shop there was an old corrugated iron gate. Beyond the gate there was a narrow passage way, which led to a tiny courtyard. On the left side of the yard there was a doorway that led into a garage-like room. When I entered it I was surprised to find that it was furnished and that it had a neat and pleasant appearance. The furniture was second-hand: a single bed, a wooden table and three chairs, and, dominating everything else, a single waist-high bookcase with its shelves tightly packed with a large assortment of paperbacks, including *The Fountainhead*.

These books really surprised me; I hadn't seen so many paperback novels in one single room before. I knew

147

Ponsammy, who lived in Jerusalem Street and who was a Swaraj official — I went to his place sometimes when Swaraj held meetings there — had a tall glass bookcase that contained titles such as *The Wisdom of India*, *Gandhi*, *J.C. Smuts*, *M.K. Sastri* and dictionaries, encyclopaedias and very thick tomes, which, I was sure, nobody had, would or could read. But here the books, I could see, had been read. The idea that someone of my age actually bought and read books astounded me — and a fellow like Sattar. I had the impression that nothing interested Sattar. He was a Memon and the only thing the Memons cared for was making money. I couldn't understand it.

"Hey, Sattar you've got quite a few books."

He smiled and proposed, easy and friendly, "if you want to borrow any of them, you're more than welcome, you know."

As our relationship grew, I discovered, contrary to all my expectations, that he was a wonderfully sincere, intelligent, broadminded and kind person — a rare phenomenon among the otherwise penny-pinching, dour and bigoted Memons. Soon he came to know and to befriend everybody at 226. In time, I came to know everybody at his place, but they being more orthodox and conservative (his parents were born in India, his mother spoke no English, and his father never left the shop), I only had a chance to meet his elder sister, who was also like him, friendly and generous. She often came into the room bearing a tray with sweet tea and biscuits. I would have liked to have known her better. But it wasn't accepted that a single Muslim woman should speak at length with any male, especially with a non-Muslim male; so my acquaintance with her remained distant and superficial.

* * *

Changes occurred in school when I was in standard eight. A law passed by the government decreed that Indian teachers should teach Indians and white teachers should teach whites. When the year started Mrs Botha, Mrs Van der Walt, Mrs Armoury, Mrs Wymann, Mrs Dougall, Mr Van Dyk, Mr

148

Strauss and another Hollander, Mr Hoekstra (whom we never had but who, for all that, formed an integral part of the School) were absent and, as far as the School was concerned, gone forever. In their place came Mr Dockrat, Mr Carami, Mr Ebrahim, Mr Singh, Mr Kota, Mr Vello and Mr Naidoo. The principal, Mr Caulineck, and the vice principal, Mr Brown, however, stayed on.

There was talk that the standard of education would decline. I overheard Nooradeen Mansoor, a Prinsloo Street fellow, asserting, "My father says that Indian teachers can never be as good as white teachers." In spite of these misgivings Indian teachers settled down nicely and we settled down nicely with them. The stuffiness and the stiffness in school-life disappeared. The tension between white and black, so characteristic of life in Pretoria, evaporated; even so, I missed Mr Strauss and Mrs Van der Walt.

The year ended and I passed smoothly to standard nine. But I remember Ahmedie (who was then in standard ten, the all-important matric class) warning Ebies and myself: "OK, standard eight is different from standard seven, but standard nine is really different from standard eight. I'm not joking, you guys will have to buck up if you want to pass." He wasn't the only one to warn us thus; at the Corner the few that had made matric also emphasized how enormous the gap between standards eight and nine was. Scared by all the forebodings, I made up my mind to make an extra effort for that last but one year at school.

I, who had always longed to learn a European language, was excited and enthusiastic when Mr Brown introduced Latin to the School. I was in standard seven then and I assumed, because people referred to Latin America and to the Latin-speaking people of Europe, that Latin was a language that the Europeans used like they did German or Spanish. Gradually, however, I learnt that it was nothing of the sort. This recognition persuaded me that it was the old Indian thing again: hanging on to a dead past, holding on to outdated values and fastening on to things that had no relevance to the present. Why couldn't they teach Italian or French; that way I would, at least, be able to understand (if not talk to) those recently

149

arrived Continentals. I lost interest in Latin and, since for standard eight it neither counted for the exams nor appeared on the progress cards, I discounted it altogether.

Now in standard nine, on the first day, my class mates and I were asked if we wanted to do Latin as an exam subject. I was aware of Mr Brown's argument: "Knowledge of Latin helps your English because there are many words in the English language which have a Latin origin." But I wasn't convinced; the reasoning struck me as being long cut and topsy-turvy. Isn't it, I told myself, like saying sheep eat grass, therefore, if you want to appreciate your mutton chop better, learn to savour the taste of grass. I said, no, in spite of the class's majority view.

Patrick, Ebies, Neelen, some others and myself, the Don't-want-to-do-Latins, were sent (demoted would have been the more accurate word) to standard nine B. I became aware of the unexpected rupture between myself and the class I had joined eight years ago when I gathered my things and was about to leave it. I looked at the familiar and distinct faces of Mansoor Omar, Sattar Aboobaker, Jagdish Joshi, Dayal Bhana, Wei Leen, Premlal Patel and Yusuf Joosub and felt, though I was aware they weren't real friends, that something more than a mere separation was taking place. When I reached the stairs and saw the wall clock and the hand-painted portrait of Gandhi, I suddenly felt sad.

* * *

Mr Dida, on the first day of our history class, gave standard nine B a sermon about working hard, and as he did so, handed each of the students an exercise book. We wondered what was happening, for we were already in possession of our history notebooks. "This is your assignment book. For your first assignment I want you to write everything you can on Louis Trichardt's Trek. Read Walker's *A History of South Africa*, and his *Great Trek*, and, if possible, Geen. You'll find copies in the library. You have lots of time. I'm giving you six weeks. Be warned, those who fail to give me the assignment will not fail to receive three of the best from me."

Six weeks later, since none of us had the wish to acquaint ourselves with Mr Dida's cane, we all without exception gave in our assignments. Three weeks later they were marked and returned. The worst essay was given out first. Mr Dida, seated behind his rectangular, wooden table, called out: "Premlal Bhana?" Someone in the middle row at the back of the class timidly raised his hand.

"One out of ten. Disastrous. Pull your socks up, boy, if you want to go to standard ten!"

"Ram Naidoo?" He surveyed the class, waiting with that look, which seemed to say: Now, who's this monkey who doesn't even know his own name?

Naidoo lifted his hand, even more timidly than Bhana.

"One and a half out of ten. Two and a half pages. If you really tried you could have written, at least, double that amount. This won't do boy! This won't do!"

Mr Dida, sensing he was wasting his time, now, without lifting his head, simply read out the name of the assignment-book owner, and, with hardly a pause, made his dry-toned comment: "Ebrahim Mohamed, one and a half out of ten. A good introduction but all the rest is simply nonsense!"

"Patrick Jackson, one and a half out of ten. If you paid as much attention to your assignment as you do to girls, you could have had six or seven out of ten. You'd better forget the girls for this year — if you want to pass!

"Tayob Moosa, two out of ten. More time in the School library, boy, and less in the bioscopes. Book up with the Royal, the Empire and the Orient for the holidays, now it's time to work!

"Sanu Chetty, three out of ten. Well, you've got the ability to produce something worth while, but I know you have to go and sell samoosas and moorkoo for your mother. Sooner or later, boy, you'll have to make a choice between selling and studying."

And so it went. Nobody got more than four and half out of ten. Finally he got to the last book. Then with a deadpan expression on his face, he picked it up, walked towards where Patrick and I were seated, and dropped it on the desk without comment. I was astonished, and so were the rest of the class. True, I had worked on the assignment and had writ-

151

ten almost eighteen pages but when he started giving out the books, my confidence waned. I was sure that like everybody else I, too, had somehow made a mess of it. I opened the book and quickly turned the pages until I got to the end of the essay. Eight. I couldn't believe it but when I read Mr Dida's comment, it was obvious that he couldn't believe it either: "Excellent. I hope this is all your own work."

My results at the end of the term were good. With three others I was promoted to standard nine A. When I protested that I wanted to stay in standard nine B, Mr Dida told me I had no choice. When I further protested that standard nine A did Latin and that I didn't want to do Latin, I was told that nine A had dropped Latin.

* * *

In the second half of that year, Mr Dockrat, our English teacher, gave us an essay assignment: "The exemplary life of Albert Schweitzer (or David Livingstone, Louis Pasteur or Marie Curie)." I knew little about any of them. But I managed to obtain the one book in the School library on the life of Louis Pasteur, but, after glancing through it, I wasn't won over to the subject. I finally wrote about David Livingstone because Khrishnaner had a book, *Livingstone the Liberator*, which he was prepared to forgo for a week or so. I was on the point of returning the Pasteur book to the library when Raymond Ernest called at 226.

It was a windy crisp July afternoon. I was seated at the dining room table looking through an atlas trying to find out where Kuruman was situated when I heard someone ring the front door bell. I recognized Raymond immediately. We knew each other by sight. In fact, we were together for a short while in standard nine B, although we had hardly noticed each other. But I knew he had an elder brother, a step brother, who was called Stanley, and that Stanley was half-Tamil (his father was one of the Orient Brothers), and his mother, a handsome, light-skinned round woman, was "Coloured"; and that the same mother had another child from a Khoja fellow and that this child was Raymond Ernest.

152

"Are you Jay Naidoo?" I found the question strange. Everybody knew who I was or, at least, that is what I thought, and yet Raymond's question had no trace of teasing and was evidently sincere.

I smiled a little disconcertedly and said, "Yes." I could see that Raymond wanted to talk to me; so I asked him to come in. I made him see that I was busy but I also made him understand that he wasn't really disturbing me.

"Hey, you know we have to do this English assignment for Dockrat. When I tried to get the book on Pasteur, Mr Velloo told me that you had already taken it out.

"Yes, I've got it."

"Hell man, do a guy a favour! Can I borrow it off you for a few days? Or can I have it after you've finished with it — that is, if you'll be finished with it soon?"

"Well, you can have it now if you want. I'm not going to use it."

He looked at me as if I had hit him over the head. This initial meeting started up a friendship between us. Raymond had the reputation of being, as the Location was wont to put it, half-cracked. I didn't find anything that was looney in him; on the contrary I found his humour mischievous and intelligent.

I always remember his story of a couple of newly-weds.

"Nah, man Jay, you see this guy he meets this cherrie. And she's really lekker and all that, you know man. And she speaks English to him, only English. I mean she's really a civilized chick. You know, no fuckings, no blerrys, no voetseks, no bliksems, no hey jongs, no pas ops — none of that shit comes out of her mouth. And she never, never uses a single word of the Boer language. You know, really man, an angel of a woman. And this guy he courts her, you see, and, you know how it is, birds and bees and all that crap. He puts a ring on her finger. After the wedding they come home and then she tells him, out of the blue like that: 'Hey, wat maak jy? Bliksem, jy drink nie vanaand nie, jong!' He displayed a broad smile. I couldn't help laughing. He looked at me and said: "Hey Jay, you have to watch out, women; I'm telling you, man — you can't trust them!"

153

23

"What a fall was there!" These were Mr Dida's words just before he handed me my progress card. It was, I remember now, the second period of the last day of the term, a glorious early autumn day; and, since it was still in the morning, my brain was clear and unhindered by the post-break drowsiness. I sat there and looked at my card, oblivious to the reaction of the others or to what Mr Dida was telling them. From standard six to standard nine my card had never had a single red ring but now, in standard ten, I had five rings out of a possible six. I had failed in Afrikaans, in Arithmetic and Bookeeping, in Mathematics, in Physical Science, and in History. The only subject I managed to pass, and there too, I just scraped through, was English. Yes, there was a fall all right.

Why the disaster? Was it related to my father's death? I clearly recollected that while "Old Block's" body lay in the sitting room I was busy revising my notes for the second term exam. In spite of the turmoil I experienced then, I remember I had to perform a ceremony fourteen days after the death at the river side at day break, and when I got to school that morning, I had already lost fifteen minutes of my history-exam time — and yet I did pretty well in those exams. No, I couldn't blame anybody but myself. I thought of Shakepeare's *Julius Caesar*, one of our English set books for matric, and I recalled another quote:

The fault, dear Brutus, is not in our stars,
But in ourselves ...

There had been no final term exam at the end of standard nine. After the second term the teachers decided that they

154

knew who deserved and who didn't deserve to go on to matric. I was led to understand that I was one of those that had already merited a place for the future matric class. Perhaps the strain of the second term did have something to do with my fall, but I was aware that I had resolved to coast along; so when the exams came, I did no revising and treated the papers, except for English, with little regard.

In that last year in school, by the luck of the draw, Raymond and I had been respectively selected to represent the two matric sections in an oral examination — Raymond for arts and I for science. We were thrown together in front of an officious white examiner. Mr Dockrat had explained to the respective classes, some time before, that all of us would have to prepare our prose and poem recitations and be prepared to read a passage from one of our set books. It was, for all that, quite a coincidence. The two of us were still in the formative period of our friendship; so we sat in the august and foreboding atmosphere of the principal's office, the place you came to when you were caught out in a first grade delinquency, and waited, revising our respective pieces, in expectant silence.

The white examiner sat behind the principal's desk, glum, cold and remote. I was grateful that he didn't look frightening. Then he started moving, shuffling his papers and, finally, he spoke. Looking at Raymond, he said: "Are you J. Naidoo?"

"No sir, I'm R ... Raymond Ernest."

"Oh, I see. Yes. All right, Ernest, what poem have you chosen?"

"'The Charge of the Light Brigade' by Lord Tennyson, sir."

"Yes. And you, Naidoo?"

"'Elegy Written in a Country Church-yard' by Thomas Gray, sir." I was going to say 'Gray's Elegy' but I thought it best to repeat the title the same way Raymond had done.

"Well, shall we start with you Naidoo?"

"Yes, sir."

The curfew tolls the knell of parting day,
The lowing herd winds slowly o'er the lea,
The plowman homeward plods his weary way,
And leaves the world to darkness and to me ...

I made a conscious effort to pronounce the words correctly. I was aware that I would be impatient to get the whole thing over and done with; so I took care to let the words flow out rather than spill out. I didn't look at the examiner but focussed instead on the top of the wall, at the point where it met the ceiling. For a fraction of a second I felt as if I was in the Temple and back at Tamil School. Raymond remained seated on one of the twin wooden chairs that were obviously there for those who came to visit the principal.

Learning things off by heart always vexed me. I think it was this which made me slightly hostile to poetry but I did like Gray's Elegy. It seemed to express so many of the things I felt. I was particularly fond of the lines:

Full many a gem of purest ray serene,
The dark unfathom'd caves of ocean bear:
Full many a flower is born to blush unseen
And waste its sweetness on the desert air.

The dark unfathom'd caves and desert air so appropriately described the Location. And I felt that in the domain of football Veegee, Dickie, Bagus, Issie and Gona were flowers born to blush unseen.

I didn't blunder or stumble. My delivery was correct and relatively convincing. But Raymond's performance was of another order.

Half a league, half a league
Half a league onward,
All in the valley of Death
Rode the six hundred ....

Theirs not to make reply,
Theirs not to reason why,
Theirs but to do and die.

It was delivered with verve and extravagance — it was splendid. I spied the examiner, he had been looking at Raymond's book and following the lines of the handwritten

156

poem. He now lifted his head and looked at Raymond, as if to verify that the sounds he was hearing were indeed coming from Raymond's lips.

"Yes," the examiner said, which to my ear sounded false; for he too had been impressed and now here he was trying to feign indifference. I avoided Raymond's beaming and ecstatic eyes.

"Well Naidoo, what choice have you made for your prose passage?"

"I have a passage from Charles Dickens' *David Copperfield*, sir."

"Yes, and you Ernest?"

"I have one from Daniel Defoe's *Robinson Crusoe*, sir."

"All right, Naidoo, will you start then."

"Yes, sir."

The first objects that assume a distinct presence before me, as I look far back, into the blank of my infancy, are my mother with her pretty hair and youthful shape, Peggotty, with no shape at all, and eyes so dark that they seemed to darken their whole neighbourhood in her face, and cheeks and arms so hard and red that I wondered the birds didn't peck her in preference to apples ....

I hadn't read the book but Mrs Botha spent five to ten minutes every Monday to Friday throughout standard six reading from *David Copperfield*. The book was so familiar that I had the impression I had read it myself; and I was always struck by the figure of Peggotty and attracted to the passage which compared her redness to an apple's. This complexion, which was so different from ours, evoked wondrous pictures of the English, and of England.

My performance was once again clear and correct. Raymond's performance, his loud and highly expressive voice accompanied this time by dramatic gestures, was even more astonishing.

I stood like one thunderstruck, or as if I had seen an apparition. I listened, I looked round me, I could hear nothing, nor see anything. I went up to a rising ground, to look farther. I went up

157

the shore, and down the shore, but it was all one; I could see no other impression but that one. I went to it again to see if there were any more, and to observe if it might not be my fancy; but there was no room for that, for there was exactly the very print of a foot — toes, heel, and every part of a foot ....

I wanted to rub my eyes and wring my ears to make sure that what I was seeing and hearing was, indeed, real. I suspected that my mouth must have, at one moment, dropped open, for the examiner's eyes caught mine and seemed to suggest: well, you needn't look so surprised. It would have been possible, whenever Raymond stopped to catch his breath or mark a pause, to have heard that old pin drop.

I had a copy of Thackeray's *Henry Esmond* from which I had selected a passage I was going to read. Raymond did the same with Shaw's *Pygmalion*. These were two of our English set books. But for some reason the examiner didn't ask us to read.

When we came out, I couldn't decide whether Raymond had been mad or masterly. Anyway, I congratulated him, half in sincerity, half in derision; but he accepted it at its face value. Later that day, Mr Dockrat congratulated us in front of the whole class: "Thanks to Ernest and Naidoo all of you have, for your orals, an above average pass mark."

* * *

In the meanwhile, outside school an atmosphere of tension and crisis predominated. Verwoerd withdrew from the Commonwealth — I remember Mr Dida, during the history lesson, reading the announcement from that morning's *Rand Daily Mail* — a huge stay-at-home strike slogan was daubed on the side of a house in Blood Street, the names of Nelson Mandela and Robert Sobukwe, and of Poqo and Umkhonto we Sizwe became current; and a year earlier, the year when "Old Block" was no more, there were the events of Sharpeville and Langa, the march on the Cape Town police station, and the banning of the ANC and PAC.

But the long, difficult year came to an end. I remember the

red letter day — the day when the matriculation results were about to be released. I recall now how I consciously set out to de-dramatize the event: I affected nonchalance. Maybe I was scared, maybe I wanted to be different from the others or maybe I understood that what had to be had to be. I recalled the words of Doris Day's song:

> Chê sara sara,
> whatever will be will be.
> The future is not ours to see,
> Chê sara sara.

I went to the cinema, to the Royal. It was a hot December afternoon; as usual the cinema was crowded, uncomfortable and stuffy with the heavy odour of tobacco and dagga. I partly watched and partly slept through the first feature, Ray Danton in *The Fever in the Blood*. After the interval I had the usual Tingaling ginger beer and salted peanuts, then I watched the second film, Raf Vallone in *A View from the Bridge*. The tragic and violent end — I never liked films where the hero gets killed — left me feeling sad and withdrawn.

I knew that about this time the results would be out but, committed as I was to the resolution of not getting excited, I proceeded with the routine of my afternoon training session. When I had reached the seventh of my ten-exercise course, the sit up, Sattar entered the room. He appeared then, as was his wont on eventful occasions, highly excited; his rotund figure, his boyish face and his slightly effete movements were all greatly agitated. He gave me the results and congratulated me with a handshake. Sattar had passed but he wasn't entirely satisfied with his results. He had hoped to further his studies at Wits University and for this it was absolutely necessary for him to have outstanding marks — entrance into this white university was a privilege allowed only to the very best of us "non-whites" — so I hesitated about congratulating him. Raymond Ernest, unfortunately, ploughed in English.

My uncles and aunts, my brother and sisters, and my

mother were all visibly proud of me. I realised that in their eyes I was unique; for none in the family, near or remote, had as yet achieved such an educational feat. My results weren't exceptional and yet I had this sensation of self-satisfaction and fulfillment because, ever since that day Mr Dida had announced my fall, I had secretly resolved that I would obtain a pass, and this is what I had done.

My mother decided, the family decided and, I suppose, necessity decided that I would become a teacher. I recalled I had told Soobathie's parents that I wanted to become a clerk for some wholesale firm. I thought about this alternative, and I thought about the image of the local teachers, which was not, after all, a very flattering one. In the end, the pull of circumstances and the weight of family opinion made me decide against being a clerk. I consoled myself: as a teacher I'd have half days from Monday to Thursday and, on Fridays, I'd stop at eleven o'clock in the morning. And the paid holidays and the security were conditions not to be demeaned. How many times people had told me: "At least, if you're a teacher you know your job is safe."

I settled down to some clear and cold thinking. There was a single college in Fordsburg catering for all the matriculants of the Transvaal for that year and, in some cases, for the previous year as well, which meant that at least a hundred students would be applying, and only a maximum of thirty of these would be accepted. It was obvious that getting into the College wasn't going to be easy.

It was essential to have a clear matric pass and a good record at school testifying to sound character. Both these all the students applying had. But what, in the end, counted was the impression the student made with the College Committee during the obligatory interview session. Two men in that vital Committee of eight were Indians.

My Uncle Rajee said he had a distant relative, who was also a business associate, living in Lenasia. My uncle was quite convinced that a visit to him would improve my chances at the interview. I was innocent enough to think that one was chosen on merit and on merit alone. The idea of making contact with a member of the Selection

Committee, even indirectly, hadn't occurred to me. But seeing that no harm could come from such a trip, I went along. Besides, I hadn't been to Lenasia or to Lenz, as the locals called it, and I was quite eager to see the township that was causing such a rumpus among the Indians dreading the effects of the government's Group Areas Act.

A few days later we went to Lenz. The man we visited was himself a teacher. He made a vague promise of letting Mr Pradesh, the man on the Selection Committee, know that I was a worth-while candidate. But I got the impression that he was embarrassed by the visit and by its oblique suggestion of wire-pulling.

Lenz, it was obvious, was in the making. Piles of cement, pyramids of brick, mounds of sand and a plethora of other building material (never seen in the Location because nothing was ever built, altered or repaired there) littered the back and front of the half-finished houses and the vacant plots of land. Already the embryonic town was splitting itself into sections of rich and poor. The house we visited was new, well-furnished, larger and better planned than the houses built and let by the municipality. The slum section, the area where the poor made their homes in an abandoned army barracks, the area that I had heard so much about, never came into view. Lenz was far more extensive than I had been led to expect. The barrack-slum had obviously been swallowed up by the general sprawl. Only someone well-acquainted with the new township would have been able to locate it.

The visit made me conscious of the task lying ahead. Previously, I had thought it enough to present myself to the Selection Committee, to be as frank as possible and to answer questions off the cuff. This wasn't so at all. My enquiries, from various sources, especially from those who had already been successful in getting into the College, indicated otherwise. Ahmedie, who was in the third and final year of the teachers' course, counselled me thus: "Make sure you're dressed at your sober best. Don't be casual. Dress conservative. Wear a neat tie and put a white shirt on. You've got a blazer, haven't you?"

"Yes'.

"Well, put that on. You must emphasize your sporting abilities both real and false. It's a pity Swaraj doesn't have a monogram to put on to your breast pocket. Hey! Rangers have got one! You could borrow one from somebody in the team or from one of their supporters."

"Yes, I know Ismail Jeeva has got one; and I don't think he'd mind lending it to me. But Rangers, Ahmedie, how can I wear a Rangers monogram?"

Ahmedie gave me a look which suggested that I still had a lot to learn, and said: "What do they know? They'll see the monogram and it'll impress them. If they ask you about it, you'll tell them a story about your exploits as a Rangers player.

"Tell them you're interested in physical culture, that you organised and now run a bodybuilding club, and tell them you take part in many youth activities. Tell them you read a lot. And, if they ask you why you want to become a teacher, tell them that you had always wanted to be a teacher. Tell them that you come from a family that has a long line of teachers."

I was flabbergasted. Ahmedie broke off his directive and, with a tone of mature inevitability, said: "Yes, you've got to lie, and you've got to praise yourself like you've never thought of praising yourself before. Make yourself sound good — after all, that is what the interview is all about!"

24

"What does the R on your monogram stand for Mr Naidoo?" someone asked.

"The R just before FC!" someone else stressed.

For a fraction of a second I was lost but then I recovered my wit and came back quickly: "Rangers — Rangers Football Club."

The white man, who had asked the first question, asked another: "Are you a footballer, then?"

"Yes, sir. Rangers is a first division team in the Pretoria District Football Association and I've been a regular first-team player for the past four years." I saw they wanted me to go on, so I added: "I've represented the Pretoria eleven in several inter-city games, and I've been the captain of the Pretoria Indian High School team for four consecutive years." I felt certain that all this impressed them.

I remember it was a January day in 1962 and I was four months from my twenty-first birthday. I remember how the College came into view just as I emerged from a sinister, ill-lit and ill-smelling subway. When I first saw it with its assemblage of grey pre-fab stalag buildings, huddled together on a stark cement surface and demarcated by a bare wire fence, I was, to say the least, disappointed. I compared it with the Pretoria High School and found it wanting. There were no trees, no hedges, no lawns and no flower beds. It wasn't even independent: it shared its grounds with the Johannesburg High School. Still, I allowed sheer optimism to brush these first negative impressions aside.

Innie, who had finished his matric before I did, had applied to the College but he had failed his interview. So he got a job as a clerk with Pretoria Tobacco. I hadn't seen him for almost a year — now he, too, was there making a second attempt to get into the College. We caught sight of each other early on the first morning. I think he was staying with his sister in Fordsburg, so we didn't travel together by train. He greeted me but it was a very formal greeting. I responded in kind. He moved within a new circle of friends. I felt loath to force his company.

We were called to the principal's office in alphabetical order but not knowing how long each interview would last, I, like everyone else, hung about the College. Apart from going to Cisco's, one of the two cafés opposite the College, there was nothing else to do but to bide my time. Some of the fatigue and lassitude of the wait was relieved by the Fordsburg High School girls who passed the grounds of the College on their way to their school.

My turn finally came just after three o'clock. As I walked towards the office, the strains of 'A Whiter Shade of Pale', which seemed to be the only record Cisco's had in their jukebox, kept weaving through my anxious thoughts.

The office I entered was matter of fact with little or no signs of learning or study. The men seated behind and around the edges of a large rectangular table looked grave and patriarchal. Patel, one of the two Indian men — he was surprisingly Dravidian in colour — had a greyish moustache and a balding head. The other, who obviously was Mr Pradesh, wore thick-rimmed tortoiseshell spectacles and had a surly, unfriendly face. Both of them had that unmistakable school authority written all over them — rigid and uncomfortable sitting postures and sombre suits with matching waistcoats. And yet both in the presence of their fellow white Committee members seemed submissive and self-effacing. Someone, I didn't notice who, invited me to sit down.

One of the white men, almost in a friendly tone, addressed me: "So, Mr Naidoo, can you tell us what makes you want to become a teacher? When, in fact, did you first think of teaching?"

God, how nervous and tense I was then. I remember a whole colony of butterflies fluttered and whirred about in my stomach and, without noticing it, I was beginning to rub

164

my hands together, as if I was rolling a bit of clay between my palms. Even worse, I felt a sudden and pressing need to *chore*. I pressed my knees together and ripped my thoughts away from the discomfort. Even so, I felt tiny drops of sweat forming on my forehead. I began to speak.

"Actually, I can't remember when I didn't want to be a teacher. I suppose my two uncles, who are teachers, persuaded me to their vocation even before I realized there were other professions to consider. It was also my mother's wish that I become a teacher." I was going to stop at that point when suddenly I realized there was something I had almost forgotten to mention. "There is also the fact that I think I'm temperamentally fitted to become a teacher. I know this because I've done some soccer coaching and I found that I nearly always obtained the results I sought."

This bit was partly false or rather exaggerated but I remember I was hoping I could steer the interview towards sport, where I would be able to talk with greater ease and fewer lies.

Someone, after those questions about Rangers and football asked me if I played any other sport. I replied that I ran the hundred yards.

"What time do you clock?"

"Oh, it's difficult to say, I was only clocked once and, if I am not mistaken, it was very near ten seconds."

This answer worried me. On reflection I wondered if this wasn't a bit too fantastic. I knew I had to tell them I was good but I couldn't very well claim I was Superman. To my relief, I found out later that ten seconds for a hundred-yard dash was a damn good time but not an impossible one to achieve.

Several more questions followed and then the final question came from the principal, Mr Stallwart, a bespectacled man, who looked like a pukka British army officer: "What was the last book you read, Mr Naidoo?"

"*Something of Value* by Robert Ruark," I shot back.

"Why did you choose to read that particular book?"

"Well, I like going to the cinema and I knew there was this controversial film, called *Something of Value*, which featured Rock Hudson. But I don't know why exactly the film was banned for non-whites; so, curiosity, I suppose, got the better of me. I wanted to know what the film was all about and as a consequence I bought the paperback and read it."

"Did you like the book?" Mr Stallwart asked, as if he was preparing the ground for another question.

"Yes. It was easy to read and the story was very good." Then came the unexpected: "What did you think of the Mau Mau?"

The novel portrayed the Mau Mau as blood-thirsty savages and as ritual cannibals motivated only by mischief and murder. I was shocked by the cruelty and the ghoulishness of the blood oaths and, yet, incoherently and spontaneously, I sympathized with them. I felt for them what I felt for the American Indians when I saw Burt Lancaster in *Apache*.

I winced, contorted my mouth into a sour expression (I was at that moment thinking of the blood oaths) when Mr Stallwart, impatient to come to my assistance, said, "You didn't like them, did you?"

"No, sir!" I said vigorously and shook my head emphatically.

The more I shook my head the more they smiled with approval and satisfaction.

Wise now to the kind of answer they wanted, I came back decisively and said, "No. I wouldn't like to have anything to do with them."

My declaration tilted the prevailing staid and stand-offish atmosphere. The men, the white men, looked like cricket enthusiasts who had just seen one of their batsmen hook one for six.

Someone asked me if I had read anything else. I said, "Yes, *Shaka Zulu*."

This was a lie. I had seen the book in the window of Chiba's Café on several occasions. The cover caught my eye. There was this superbly proportioned Zulu warrior, magnificently decked out in plumes and beautifully bearing a shield and an assegai; but I never found the courage to go into the shop and actually buy the book. I suppose, I wasn't truly interested in the contents.

"Do you know who wrote it?" I had hardly noticed the

166

name of the author. I pretended as if the name was on the tip of my tongue. It must have been convincing, for one of them came to my rescue and said: "Oh, it doesn't matter, it's Ritter."

They thanked me, said I could go and added that they would let me know in a few days time. They did. I was accepted. Was this due, I wondered, to the trip to Lenz or to my performance during the interview?

* * *

Everything about going to College was new. It was exciting to get up early in the morning, round about five o'clock, and to catch that twenty-past-five Putco bus. It was a new experience to sit there on those rigid wooden seats and share the bus with young male and female Indian and "Coloured" workers. I spied the looks of the passengers. Their expressive faces all seemed to suggest that life could no longer surprise them. There was a special atmosphere in that bus. I didn't quite know what it was — perhaps a certain gritty quality borne out of independence and tough work conditions — but something in that bus made me feel very young and very immature. Some of the commuters were alive, awake and engaged in full discussion; others, especially the older men, played cards; others again, those who had had a long night, tried to sleep but it was blowing against the wind: the green bus had an evil rattle. The Putco vehicle left Jerusalem Street, just outside Mohideen's Café, made several stops (most of the passengers seemed to have got on at Cowie and Struben Streets) before it came to a final and swishing halt outside the Pretoria Railway Station. I noticed that the space Paul Kruger's statue occupied, when I travelled to Johannesburg once before, had now been replaced by a small square.

The moment I left the bus, a cold, metallic sensation invaded my insides and seemed, uncannily, to displace the warm feeling that had hitherto been nestling there. I saw the sand-coloured building and the entrance on the left marked *Whites Only* and *Blankes Alleen*. I was surprised to find that the separate flows of whites and blacks, once they had

167

entered the station, came together as they all headed towards the same platform.

I spotted the newspaper and confectionery kiosk and decided I would go and buy myself a *Rand Daily Mail*. I cheerfully approached the white female assistant behind the counter. She greeted me with an icy stare and said, spitting the words out, "We don't serve non-whites here!"

God, how I hated getting caught out like that. I gave up the idea of getting a paper and followed the others into the first class non-white carriage. I found a seat next to Saapaa Dhida, a lanky, All Bharats footballer who, to my surprise, had become in the past two years a junior national tennis star. I didn't say anything to him except to greet him and to ask him if the seat was free. Saapaa took out a paperback. I was astonished to see that it was *Lady Chatterley's Lover*. I had heard so much about the book and was convinced that it had been banned. Although Saapaa was already deep into his reading, I couldn't help interrupting him: "Hey Sapps, isn't that thing you're reading banned?"

"Nah, not now. It was, but not now." I had just seen Horst Buchholz in *Nine hours to Rama*. In the film he kills Gandhi, and now when I looked at Saapaa, the mouth, the hairstyle, the voice and the skin colour all reminded me of the celluloid Gandhi. I hesitated about telling him this. Instead I looked up and saw that the carriage was already full and that the passengers coming in were forced to stand.

"Hey Sapps, isn't there another carriage?"

"For non-whites?"

"Ja."

"Yes, but they're all third class."

I felt like getting out and having a closer look at the train. I asked Saapaa if my seat would be safe.

"Oh, don't worry I'll put my briefcase here, nobody will take it!"

I had only the vaguest idea of what time the train left, so I inquired.

"Two minutes past six — we've still got ten minutes."

I checked the time on my wrist watch. The movement of passengers, swirling into and flowing out of the Station,

168

dominated sight and sound. I left the carriage and moved towards the right. I noticed there were three or more third-class carriages. The seats inside were, like those of the Putco buses, stiff, hard and made of wood. The carriages were also overcrowded. Most of the passengers inside were Africans; there was a sprinkling of "Coloureds" but no Indians. When I returned to the first class carriage, I noticed, for the first time, that most of the passengers were Indians. The flagrant difference between the third class and the first class surprised me. I felt uncomfortable, a feeling of culpability seized me until I told myself: *Ag, but it's not for me to reason why* — I still had Raymond Ernest on my mind.

I noticed the whites had to go past the non-white carriages in order to reach their side of the train. I moved back from the carriage and watched the forbidden, the untouchable European world go by. The men looked unattractive. Their clothes were ill-fitting and the colour of the garments were ill-matched. The more I saw of them the more I was struck by their dreary severity.

The women were quite different. Was it their delicate skins, their scented clothes, their perfumed bodies, their fleshy legs, their exposed feet, their varnished nails, their powdered faces, their painted lips or their different coloured hair and eyes, which made them so attractive and desirable? Alas, they passed by hurriedly, arrogantly and indifferently, as if I was an object, something functional and nondescript: a platform bench or a wastepaper-basket. But the swish of their dresses and the rustle of their skirts sent a current through my body. The scent of their deodorants and perfumes roused secret emotions and produced a delicate sense of illicit intimacy.

"Hey Jay," Saapaa hollered, "you'd better get in — the train's gonna leave!"

* * *

A week later when I got on to the train — the bus had been late in getting to the station — all the seats had already been occupied. The corridor of the carriage had enough standing

169

room for at least eight passengers. I joined a group of six. I leaned against the metal-glass plating separating the corridor from the seats.

There hadn't been time to buy the *Rand Daily Mail*. I felt awkward and silly just standing there and looking blankly out of the window. I felt that I had to have something to read. I recalled that I had a letter from Bhiraj in the inside pocket of my black gaberdine blazer. I took the airmail letter out and read the address: 128 Addison Gardens, Shepherd's Bush, London W.14. I felt warm and special because I actually knew somebody in England. I looked at the crisp and light pale blue paper in my hand and told myself: Imagine this thing comes direct from England. I stroked the paper and tried to picture number 128. I couldn't quite fathom the word Gardens. It can't just be a street? And Shepherd's Bush made me think of the lines of the psalm that Mr Dockrat had given the standard nine class to learn as a poem:

The Lord is my shepherd
I shall not want

I read the letter carefully for the umpteenth time and stopped for the umpteenth time when I came to the words: *Here I'm living in light; there you're living in darkness. You must come to England!*

It was curious how things had turned out. I was surprised at the arrival of Bhiraj's first letter — I wasn't expecting him to write to me. Our correspondence after that letter, never let up, never ceased. In one of the letters he confided that I was, apart from his family, the only other person to whom he wrote.

All his letters were enthusiastic, optimistic and forever laudatory about the absence of racialism in England. All, in one way or another, urged me to quit South Africa and to come to England. *Come you can study here for next to nothing! Come before they pass the Commonwealth Immigration Act! Come, the opportunities here are boundless!*

I carefully folded the letter and put it back into my pocket. I reached for my briefcase, which visibly bore the wear of my

170

school years, opened it and found a copy of the previous month's *Reader's Digest*. Just the thing, I thought. I liked reading the *Digest*. The travelogue sections were marvellous. One day I read an article about Venice and, for some time after that, I repeatedly imagined a series of ways of how I would receive a fortune that would allow me to make the trip to Europe and to savour the delights of wonderful Venice. These glossy and sumptuous descriptions of Rome, Paris, Lisbon, Madrid, Amsterdam and Vienna always left me with a wispy and persistent yearning to make a one-way trip to Europe, and to (what I was convinced was) the heartland of wisdom, beauty, tolerance and, above all, non-racialism.

America left me with mixed feelings. I loved American clothes and American cars but one day, quite by chance, I came across a *Digest* article describing the killing in Mississippi of Emmett Till, a young "Negro", all because he had dared to make some sort of pass at a white woman. The south of the United States struck me as being another place of suffering for the dark-skinned of the earth. No, going to the States would be like going to South Africa.

I flipped through the pages and found an article on Tibet. Better than nothing, I thought. It described the atrocities committed by the invading Chinese communists but politics was alien to my constitution. I didn't understand it and nobody in the Location had inspired me to understand it; so my thoughts turned to Patrick. He had told me just before the first term in standard nine came to an end that he and his family were moving to Canada. When the second term started, he didn't come back to School and I never saw him again. It was while I was wondering how Patrick was faring in Canada that I had this uncanny sensation that somebody was watching me.

I lifted my head slowly and caught sight of a pair of warm teasing brown eyes.

I smiled and said, "Good morning!"

"Good morning," came the reply fast and friendly.

I found Ayesha Moosa attractive from the start. I learnt that she lived in Lady Selborne. The Location had no esteem for Lady Selborne; we regarded it as a primitive place

171

because it had no water-borne sewerage, and thought it quirky because Africans, poor whites, "Coloureds" and Indians lived cheek by jowl, as if they had never heard of apartheid. I myself was struck by the coarseness of speech and the flinty behaviour of its inhabitants. I know whenever I heard one of the Lady Selborners use their African-inspired slang, I felt genteel and insecure.

Ayesha was a true native of Lady Selborne: born and bred there, she wittied the lingo of the place (as she herself would have said) with ease and verve. She was short, well-proportioned and fair-skinned. She had long, coquettish eye lashes, an extremely feminine walk, a thin, muted and pleasant voice and a look that called to the mind the words of a popular song:

Come into my house, my house,
I'm going to give you everything.

* * *

When I was a small boy, it puzzled me no end to see married men, and men married to beautiful women, look at other women, go out with other women, sleep with other women and father the children of other women. I was resolved that when I grew up, I would not imitate their shameful conduct. When, at seventeen, I saw and learnt the words of Shakespeare's sonnet:

... love is not love
Which alters when it alteration finds,
Or bends with the remover to remove.
O no, it is an ever-fixed mark.

I was at once convinced of its truth and persuaded to its wisdom. When I first found myself (and it was before I entered College) looking at other women, desiring other women and thinking about other women, I concluded (bearing in mind that Shakespeare couldn't be wrong: *If this be error and upon me proved, I never writ, nor no man ever*

172

loved) that my passion for Soobathie had altered, was bent and was removed.

I wanted to be frank and open about it. I told Soobathie about my hidden desire. I don't think she understood. I think she imagined I was a bit foolish or cranky to pay so much attention to a mere poem. We drifted apart.

Some months before an incident took place that perhaps presaged the breakup. We went to the Empire one Saturday evening. She was dressed in a close-fitting white cotton dress and I in a light green three-buttoned terylene suit. I felt buoyed up. A few months earlier I had given Soobathie a watch that I had bought with my savings. Everybody who knew anything about watches in the Location knew that the watch to have was an Omega, and this is what I got for her from one of the top jewelry shops in town. The gift delighted her and everybody else. That Saturday night she was wearing the watch.

We saw *Judgment at Nuremberg*. I remember we both liked the film. It had a cluster of stars: Spencer Tracy, Burt Lancaster, Richard Widmark, Marlene Dietrich, Shirley Winters and Montgomery Clift. I walked her home after the picture and I remember feeling a little like Spencer Tracy when he accompanied Marlene Dietrich through the night air of Nuremberg, but turning in my head were the strains not of 'Lili Marlene' but of 'Walking My Baby Back Home'. I didn't enter the house when we got to her place. Instead I kissed her good night and waited for her to pass the front door before I set off for 226.

The next evening we met, as was customary, at 226. I noticed she had a troubled look on her face. When I asked her what was up, she said, "Oh Jay, you know last night when you left me, I saw I didn't have my watch on. The only place where I could have dropped it was in the cinema. I went there with Siva but we didn't find anything."

What could I say? I didn't say, "Oh, it's nothing. I'll get you another one." It was, after all, one of those once-in-a-life-time things. I just shrugged my shoulders and suggested with gesture rather than words that it was no use crying over spilt milk.

But something after that gave way. Our meetings became less frequent, then occasional, and then finally rare, until one day I told her that our relationship had become false and that there was no point in us seeing each other any more. But she couldn't and she didn't want to understand.

The Sunday thereafter she came up to 226 to see me, as if I hadn't said anything. When I saw her, I was more peeked than taken aback. I reproached her for being stubborn and pig-headed but she brushed my objections aside.

"But can't you understand, I'm attracted to other girls now. It wasn't like that before. This can only mean one thing: our relationship is not genuine any more. I mean, how can I go out with you, marry you when I'm looking at other girls, wanting other girls. This is not the way it should be. I mean, I'm not going to be like all the others here — I'm not going to be like those men who have wives and then run around with other women. The thing has to be — oh, I don't know — well, like my parents — my father never looked at another woman."

"I don't mind if you look at other girls — if you want to go out with other girls. It's all right with me. If that is what you want."

This reply almost drove me round the bend. She didn't seem to understand anything I told her. "Look Soobathie, it's no use discussing this thing any more. I've made up my mind — I'm sorry but I must go now." I left 226 and had almost reached Lalie's Café when I noticed she was following me.

It was a warm evening, the cinemas were closed, Jerusalem Street and Grand Street were quiet, deserted. From Lalie's, the jukebox poured out the voice of Connie Francis:

Yours till the end of life's story,
This pledge to you Dear, I bring.

I turned around and said impatiently, "What are you doing?" I didn't understand her reaction. This unexpected behaviour unsettled me, made me feel uncertain. Did I really know her?

174

"Don't leave me Jay, please! Don't leave me!" Tears ran down her cheeks.

I felt sore, lousy, horrible but I told myself I had to be tough. I've got to let her know that this thing is just no good. I couldn't live a lie. Anyway, this was not the way to behave. Doing what she was doing, out in the street like that, was so common.

"Please don't carry on like this in the street! You're really forgetting yourself." She bowed her head and tried to suppress her sobs. I turned around and walked away. Sure, I felt sad, but not uncertain and never in doubt. I was comforted by the Bard:

Love alters not with his brief hours and weeks,
But bears it out even to the edge of doom.

25

At School one's religious affiliation was quite irrelevant. It was something that mattered only to adults. I remember Patrick, Ebies, Neelen and I boasted our indifference to it, but this happy period came to an abrupt end at the College. There, I belonged to a small circle of students who considered themselves not atheists but agnostics. How beleaguered we were. How distorted and misconstrued our viewpoint was rendered. How closed and immune to argument were the traditional believers in God, and how rigid, dogmatic and complacent were the Muslims. What really got me was the total absence of doubt among the majority of College students. It was the old thing again: we believe because it has been believed. If it was good yesterday, it's good today and will be good tomorrow and good for ever after.

"There must be a something, a somebody who created this world," Ahmedie used to say. None of us had an answer to that. I had read a *Digest* article refuting the case of the atheist. It also advanced the idea of the immaculate creation. There was in addition the supplementary argument of the perfect world: if the earth was a hundred yards closer to the sun it would burn up; if, on the other hand, it was a hundred yards farther away from the sun it would freeze over. Only a majestic, super being, such as what we call a God, the article argued, could create such perfection. I was convinced and yet I would have liked to have heard more about the atheists' case.

I raised this point with Ahmedie.

"Hey you know," he said, his voice excited but his face calm, "there is a thing written by Bertrand Russell that is supposed to be good. It's called *Why I'm not a Christian* but

176

impossible to get hold of here — I'm sure it must be banned."

We never found out if it was. Making inquiries of that sort was intellectual and both of us were suspicious of an intellectual approach to anything. In lieu of better information, we accepted the God idea.

My mind was hungry for new ideas, new knowledge. I remember reading Turgenev's *Fathers and Children* — Mr Van der Merwe, an Afrikaner lecturer of psychology, recommended it to us — and being impressed with the nihilist, Bazarov. Nihilist was one of the new words I learnt that year.

Ahmedie and I spent a lot of time discussing ideas. One day Ahmedie surprised me with a question:

"Jay, what divides the two of us?"

"What do you mean? You're older and I suppose I'm not a Muslim. Is that what you're getting at?"

"Ja, you know I had a long talk with my broer, Hafez, the other day. By the way do you know why they call him Hafez?"

"Nope."

"Well, if you can recite the Koran — if you know it off by heart — you become a Hafez."

I didn't say anything but it was news to me. I had never heard anybody call him anything but Hafez. What, I wondered, was his real name.

"Well, I told him about this Muslim and Hindu and Christian and I don't-know-what-else business. I mean religion divides us. Look, when I come to your place and you offer me something to eat, which, of course, is an act of generosity, what do I do? I ask you if the chicken or the meat you're offering me is halal. And this halal business, that's also another thing. You know Ahmed Akbar?"

"Ja, the guy in the second year?"

"Ja, that's right. Well, one Saturday I'm here in Cisco's. This guy Ahmed comes in, he's nice and cut and he asks for a hamburger. Basil — you know, the guy behind the counter — gets ready to prepare it for him and you know what this guy asks him: 'Is it halal?' Is it halal? I mean can you beat that — Is it halal? You see how these guys are, heh? Meat must be halal but drink, nah that's another matter — that's the kind of shit this halal business is."

"Ahmedie, if I send you a Christmas card how would you react?"

"A Christmas card? Hey, what's happening? This is not a catch, I hope?"

"No, nothing like that. Wait. Let me explain. You know last year I bought some *Digest* Christmas cards. They were nice, real sharp things. You know, famous paintings — like Leonardo da Vinci's Mona Lisa. Now, I thought it would be a good thing to send cards to the guys I was studying with — you know, I told you about this study group we had. Hell, I'm telling you I really put my foot in it. Instead of thanking me they asked me, why did I send them Christmas cards. You know, it was only then I realized that Christmas wasn't just Christmas. True's God, I took it for granted that it was a sort of end of the year thing; you know, peace, goodwill, brotherhood and all that kind of stuff."

"Well, exactly! You see what I mean; religion divides. Maybe I would have reacted like they did because each of our religions tells us we must reject the beliefs of others."

I hesitated to tell Ahmedie this, but I felt then, as I feel now, that there was a kind of tolerance among the Hindus or the Tamils that the Christians or the whites or the Muslims failed to display. I had this picture of my mother — I forget what the occasion was now — going to the Temple and the Christian church all on the same day; and I know for certain she would have gone to the Mosque (if this was allowed) and said a prayer there as well.

"Nah man, Jay, this division really bothers me. Hey, I have an idea. You know Mr Van der Merwe? We could go to him and tell him about this problem. He's OK. I'm sure he'll understand and, perhaps, he'll come up with something useful."

"Are you sure Ahmedie? I don't know about you, but I find him a little false."

"Nah, you don't know him well enough yet."

We walked towards one of the pre-fabs situated at the rear end of the College. Mr Van der Merwe was a tall youngish Afrikaner with a soft voice and a face that evoked Bradford

Dillman in the film *Compulsion*. Mr Van der Merwe sometimes held what he called cultural activities where he taught
attending students how to do Afrikaans folk dances.

I remember Ahmedie saying that Mr Van der Merwe told
them one day that he supported apartheid but in his personal
relations he wouldn't mind sharing, if he had to, a table, a
bed or whatever with a "Bantu".

"He's not like the other whites in the College," Ahmedie
stressed.

That was true enough. There was nothing stand-offish
about him, nothing of that don't-touch-me or don't-come-
too-near-me attitude so common among the whites. But
even so I couldn't quite square how one could be tolerant
towards "non-whites", as Mr Van der Merwe certainly was,
and still support apartheid.

We reached the classroom. The door was open. He was
seated at his table, leafing through a book as if he was looking for a page or a passage he had scored.

"Good morning Mr Van der Merwe!" Ahmedie said in that
way he had of sounding deferential and daring all at once. I
repeated the greeting as formally as I could and then held back.
Mr Van der Merwe didn't seem to mind our interruption.

"Come in gentlemen," he said heartily.

"Mr Van der Merwe, Naidoo and I have a problem. You
might remember, sir, we've talked a little about it before in
the class, but now I — we'd like to know what you think is
the best way to cope with it."

Mr Van der Merwe, as if he was a model of patience, listened attentively. Ahmedie's example of chicken eating, at
first, embarrassed me. Why didn't he mention marriage or
something more important, and yet when he had finished, I
felt satisfied that the problem had, after all, been successful-
ly posed.

I didn't like the smile Mr Van der Merwe had on his face.
It was, as if he was looking at Ahmedie and saying to himself, "Boy! isn't this typically Indian" or "I'll never understand these people." But his expression relaxed. He now
appeared Solomon-like and reminded me of newspaper pictures of Father Trevor Huddleston.

I was convinced that the solution to the problem Ahmedie had evoked was for us simply to ignore the religious adherences of our respective parents. If we all believed in a God, it wasn't necessary to belong either to a church or to a fixed set of beliefs. *All rivers flow to the sea;* so why the fuss. I wanted to tell Ahmedie this, but I was afraid that Ahmedie would think it far too simple. I was glad he hadn't said anything; for as I looked at Mr Van der Merwe I was confident that he, the white man, was going to suggest something wise and original. I waited for his judiciousness to fall. Mr Van der Merwe stroked his beardless chin with forefinger and thumb, his fingers were long and well manicured, and paused pensively for a few seconds before he said: "Mister Mohammed," in a soft Germanic-sounding English, "I can't really answer that question. You must present the problem to your religious leaders and ask them for an answer. What I can say for myself is this: read the Bible! I'm convinced you'll find your answer there."

* * *

Six weeks after that meeting with Mr Van der Merwe, the President and the Secretary of the Students Representative Council, Amod Jooma and Amir Addross, wanted to attend the annual NUSAS conference in Grahamstown. They hired a Volkswagen Combi and to spread the expense offered to take six other passengers with them. The trip included stops in Port Elizabeth and Cape Town; so Ahmedie, States, Boykie and I plus two others joined them. States, whose India-born father had a modest tailor shop on the corner of Lorenz and Boom Streets, was a friend of Ahmedie; Boykie was a Fordsburg fellow who I had just befriended.

In Grahamstown a NUSAS representative met us in the neat and sedate grounds of the University. We found we were going to be separated and assigned to different lodgings, where we would be living with Europeans. The idea thrilled me but also left me apprehensive. Boykie and Ahmedie were assigned to the house of a forty-year-old woman, a librarian at the University, who lived with her retired father. States

180

and I were placed with a more affluent family who lived in a large house not very far from the University. A long cinder track wound its way up to the house. Just outside the main building there was a lawn bordered by flower beds, beyond the flowers there was a cluster of leafy trees and beyond the trees, near the entrance, there was a large, garage-like room. This room, for the next few days, became our quarters.

When I saw our accommodation, I was reminded of Sattar's study room. Its isolation, independence and size were identical, except that it was more comfortable. It contained no plumbing but there was a dish and a jug filled with fresh water.

On that first night States and I were invited to the house. We walked up the pathway leading through the trees, up to the lawn and up to the building. As the double-storeyed house grew larger, a lump appeared in my throat. The African maid who met us at the door was decked out in a clean white apron. She led us quietly, and I felt condescendingly, into the sitting room.

Now when I think about it, I can't remember the details of the place except that it was rich, clean, pleasant-smelling and intimidating. I know we sat on a cloth-covered sofa and the man and his wife and their two teenage daughters sat opposite us. He was middle-aged but I can't remember his face and yet, normally, I have a memory for faces. In fact, I can't remember any of their faces. But I recollect them wearing a look of paternal friendship, mixed with curiosity, as if we were coelacanths just washed ashore. States sat there, his lips and jaw cast in cement. The coward, he saddled me with all the mouth work.

The man, like a true patriarch, did all the talking. The women, smiling with amiability, still adjusting to the novelty of our "non-white" presence, looked on in interested silence. Where do you come from? What are you studying? Have you been to the Cape before? How did you travel? How did you find the trip?

I answered these questions nervously and elliptically.

The man then told us that the room we were going to use belonged to his two sons who were down in Durban for the

181

holidays. We should, like them, enter the house whenever we wanted to use the toilet and the bathroom. We thanked them and said we would, but in our minds we knew we never would. The man then dismissed us by saying: "I suppose you boys must be feeling tired and hungry as well. What time do you have supper this evening? "

States, at last, opened his mouth and said, "At 6.30, sir."

"Oh good, you have about half an hour to visit your room and to find your way to the University canteen." Canteen, the word had a mysterious and an exotic ring to it. I imagined it to be part of the great complex world of the white man.

When States and I reached the University, Boykie and Ahmedie were waiting for us.

"Hey guys, how did it go?" Ahmedie asked.

I looked at States, indicating that I was leaving the honour of explaining to him.

"Nah, it was OK. We've got a room to ourselves; we're not in the house with the laanies."

His voice, even the others noticed, betrayed disappointment. I, on the contrary, was pleased that we were lodged apart. The tension of being daily in the house with them would have been, I felt, too much of a strain. We neither entered the house nor saw the family again. We met the African maid regularly during the five days we were there; she served breakfasts, made the beds, swept out the room, and most important of all, replaced the water.

Ahmedie and Boykie lived more intimately with the librarian and her father. They had breakfast together and discussions on everything, especially politics. After the second day States and I met Ahmedie and Boykie outside the Librarian's place.

"Hey Jay, what do you know about this country's politics?"

"The ANC and PAC are banned," I said facetiously.

"No man, be serious!"

"Well, I suppose I know as much as you do, which isn't very much."

"You see this tannie asked us: 'Do you think the non-whites have a better chance with the Liberals or the Progressives?' Hell, I'm telling you Jay, Boykie and I were at a complete loss. We didn't have a clue. Do you know what's the difference between them?"

"Well, I know this guy, Visoo Reddy, the guy who's a carpenter and who writes signs — you know, the guy who lives in Cowie Street?"

"Ja."

"Well, he's a member of the Liberal Party."

"So?"

"Well, it means that the Liberals accept non-whites."

Boykie and States didn't take part in this exchange but States suddenly reacted and said, "But maybe the Progressives accept non-whites, too; but Visoo, for some reason, didn't join them."

I looked at States, "Yes, come to think of it, you're right."

"No man," Ahmedie said impatiently, "what we have to know is what are their different ... eh ... eh — help me, I'm looking for the word ..."

"Curriculums," I said mockingly.

Ahmedie caught on at once. "Their different programs."

"Well, there's one man who'd be capable of explaining, and that's our President, Jooma," I said. But typically there was no follow up. We never found out.

It was funny. I had always wanted to meet the white world and I was then given the opportunity to do so, and yet I was incapable of taking advantage of it. I felt uncomfortable, tense, cowed, false. The others I knew, although we didn't discuss it, felt the same way.

One day we approached an attractive girl with blond hair, shapely legs and a friendly face. She was sitting on the lawn all by herself. We pretended we had just chanced upon her. We, all four of us, greeted her and inveigled ourselves into her company. We sat on the lawn but we were careful not to position ourselves too near to her. She told us she was doing a second year English and French literature course. She talked about Maupassant, Zola, Flaubert, Jane Austen, Trollope and George Eliot. As she nonchalantly reeled off these names, I looked at Ahmedie and Ahmedie looked at me. The other two seemed not to be listening. I wondered if

Ahmedie felt as I felt: this was like being asked to distinguish between the Liberals and the Progressives. We left her company as discreetly as we had joined it.

Still, the stay in Grahamstown, the one-day stop in Port Elizabeth and the four-day stay in Cape Town were eye-openers. I didn't imagine that I could in two weeks learn so much. In Grahamstown I saw a "Coloured" teacher win an English elocution contest against at least half a dozen white competitors, discovered that a canteen wasn't all it was cracked up to be, found that European food could be lousy and that I could actually miss curry, and learnt that the cinemas allowed entry to "non-whites" provided they occupied the seats in the last three rows, seats that in the Location cinemas were considered the best. In Cape Town I was pleasantly surprised to discover that the almost-tolerable racial restrictions and attitudes of the whites contrasted so dramatically with what I had seen in Natal and experienced in the Transvaal. In Cape Town too I discovered Chubby Checker and practised the twist, saw *Ben Hur* in a District Six cinema, took the cable car to the top of Table Mountain and generally learnt how ignorant I was.

Anyway, I came back with the conclusion that if things were so good in Cape Town — all the people we met there seemed to be, in contrast to Pretoria, so cultivated, so friendly and so attractive — then, surely, things must be even better overseas.

* * *

Dr Fannemeyer was the College's Afrikaans lecturer. He regularly wore, whether it was warm or cold, a woollen double-breasted suit; which was bad enough but the suit, navy blue and chalk-striped, was, on top of it, worn, creased and grease-stained. Ahmedie told me that Dr Fannemeyer was a lecturer to be respected.

"You know Jay, he looks like that but he knows a lot. He has, you know, a book that's in the reference section of the Wits library and the students there consult it," Ahmedie said with a tone of awe.

184

I must admit Fannemeyer impressed me too. I'd never before seen a white teacher dress so untidily, so negligently and with such patent lack of concern for what others, colleagues and students, thought of him. If the other lecturers tolerated him, I concluded, it must be because he was exceptional. His lecture sessions, there was no doubt, *were* exceptional. He spoke without notes, fluently, confidently and at great length, and went on regardless of attention or inattention; he wiped his chalk-stained right hand on the left sleeve of his suit jacket and every now and then went over to the metal cupboard in the corner of the classroom, brusquely took out a roll of pink toilet paper, drew out a length (the size of eight or ten sections) ripped it off with a broad movement and blew his nose with a sound equal to that of Joshua's trumpet. All, once again, with utter indifference to our presence and sensibilities.

I attended his lectures always choosing the seat nearest to the door; for once he had taken the register I slipped out without him noticing me. Sometimes, I stayed away altogether; sometimes, I came back but only to doze while he droned on. I couldn't help it but I was certain I'd reached the limit of my tolerance for Afrikaans. Do what I could I just couldn't stomach the subject.

So imagine my dread when I had, during my first practical, to give an Afrikaans lesson under Dr Fannemeyer's supervision. God! What a lesson it turned out to be. I had to explain this poem about a fly. True, I did it in a very conventional way; true, I had no heart for it and true also that anyone with a little discernment would have detected my aversion and seen through my reserve. Dr Fannemeyer told me, in the presence of six other students, that my lesson was *frot*. In fact, he didn't allow me to finish. Instead, he pushed me aside in that direct and merciless way of his and, in full view of the pupils, took over the lesson himself.

Afrikaans was going to be, there was no two ways about it, an insurmountable obstacle.

I was posted, during the second practical session, to a junior school in Benoni. There, I discovered another aspect of the teaching profession. The principal of the school was an absolute monarch and the staff were his vassals. All the teachers, without exception, I repeatedly noticed, bowed and scraped whenever they were in the presence of his majesty. Worst of all, I found myself, whenever I encountered the monarch in the playground or in the classroom, wanting to conform, wanting also to curtsy and grovel in the same way the others did, were doing and were going to do.

Before the year was out I somehow understood that I could never bring myself to teach Afrikaans; nor would I be able to accept the idea of fawning and creeping to a nincompoop simply because he happened to be a principal. I knew then that I was never going to be a teacher.

My attendance at lectures fell off and when I did attend, I took no notes. When the exams came, I had nothing to guide me, nothing to revise, nothing to study. But before then I had made up my mind that College was not for me. I decided I would work for a year, save money and then use it to go to London where I'd join Bhiraj and Innie — Innie had failed to get into the College and he had, almost in act of pique, gone off to London.

The results came out. I had failed, disastrously. Ahmedie boasted to his immediate friends: "You know, I don't know anybody except this guy (patting me on the shoulders) who actually studied to fail."

26

Leaving College was not, I discovered, all that easy. Only my close friends understood my action and sympathized with my goal. My mother was sad and disappointed. She didn't say it, not in so many words, but I knew that she felt I was tossing away the opportunity of becoming what she had always wanted me to be.

Uncle Rajee tried to dissuade me by raising the bogey of the European climate: "That place is cold, you'll freeze there!"

I remember how I looked at him. I told him with my eyes and with an expression on my face: *How do you know? You've never been there!*

"How can you leave your people behind? Your roots are here. If you don't want to become a teacher stay and find a job, do something else, but why leave for some uncertain future overseas?"

"We Indians came from India," I countered. "Our forefathers, more than a hundred years ago, took the plunge and came here. They weren't paralyzed by the unknown. And how long did they stay in Natal — was it twenty, thirty or forty years before they took the plunge again and came to the Transvaal? No, I'm not doing anything unusual. Pulling up roots is a well-established Naidoo tradition."

My uncle had no case, and he knew it.

The College itself wouldn't let me go without hindrance. Mr Stallwart requested me to return. I didn't understand why this concern was shown. Maybe my determination, my resolution, to stay away was taken as an affront to the College. The plea, however, didn't cause me to to change my mind; didn't make me waver.

Finally, I was sent a letter requesting me to meet the payment for several books I had received while I was there. I found this letter upsetting. I wanted to leave the College without a debt but I was broke. Getting a job, I was discovering, was more difficult than I had anticipated. Slowly, imperceptibly, I began to experience the life of a grown up. I wrote back promising to pay as soon as I had obtained a job, which I thought would be in a month's time.

Then one day Satchoo approached me and told me that he had this idea of opening up a photographic studio in the Location. There were already two other photographers: Sabies in Boom Street (I suspect everybody over thirty had been photographed by him) and Fine Arts in Ninth Street, but the government's Population Registration Act was coming into operation. There was a deadline and there was talk about fines for those without an identification card. People obviously were going to need photographs. In these circumstances, Satchoo thought, a third studio would be opportune.

He asked me to come in as a partner with three others. I told him, my aim was to leave the country. If he gave me a job as a darkroom assistant and photographer I'd take it, but I didn't want to be a partner. He gave me the job but stressed that I wouldn't be losing anything by being a partner. In addition to my wages, I could, he emphasized, share in the profits. I didn't want to quibble; so I allowed myself to be persuaded.

Satchoo introduced me to Natoo, the financier of the undertaking. Gona, my photographic mentor and hero, was the other person involved in the partnership. I was now just over twenty-one, Satchoo was about twenty-five, Gona was nearing thirty and Natoo was near forty. Gona had just got married, Satchoo was still a bachelor and Natoo was the father of five, and a successful businessman as well.

I learnt later that Natoo came from a dorp, Nelspruit. In that remote area the heavy conservatism of India was isolated and wholly intact. When Natoo described how he and his family cleaned their teeth Indian fashion with a twig instead of a brush and toothpaste, I was amazed. What mattered to him, he frankly owned, was Hindu tradition, his mother and money. Thanks to Natoo I, for the first time, understood what was implied when it was said that the Banias worshipped money more than they did God. How Satchoo met him I never quite found out, but it was curious that he had managed both to befriend him and to win his confidence.

Natoo on his first visit to the future studio told Satchoo, Gona and myself how all his fellow caste members of the Location had warned him not to get mixed up with the Tamils. They told him that Tamils were untrustworthy and congenitally incapable of producing the pennies let alone the pounds of profit. Natoo let us into this confidence in the hope that its revelation would reinforce our determination to prove the warning false.

When I heard it — I'm not sure how the others reacted — I felt hurt and slighted. I knew that the Hindu Gujarati businessmen kept within their own tight circle and remained aloof from the Muslims and the Tamils, but I had no idea that this seeming independence harboured a crude contempt. Maybe, among themselves, I thought, they even said that Tamils had bird brains. I forced a smile, shook my head in disbelief and asked Natoo, rhetorically, if that was really what they had said.

Natoo invested something like R500; a few alterations, to what had been a café, were required. A partition had to be put up to facilitate the dark room, and railings to provide for the background curtains and the lighting equipment; and a few darkroom accessories had to be bought — we didn't buy a camera, for we made do with Gona's Yashica twin reflex.

Just before the opening Satchoo's mother came to consecrate the studio. The nuts and bolts of Hindu ritual: camphor, coconut and the thrice repeated gesture manifested itself once again.

I recalled how my mother had consecrated the brand new, two-tone 1957 Plymouth car my father had brought home one day without announcement. Thinking such ceremonies were exclusive to non-material and festive occasions like Diwali and marriages or to sad and sombre occasions like death and burials, I asked her why she did that to a car. She replied that it would ensure the car a long life and protection from accidents. I feigned acceptance but wondered: why should camphor, coconut and triplicity prove better than correct driving and car care.

I watched Satchoo's mother going through the erstwhile movements. Less convinced than ever of their efficacy, I nevertheless refrained from criticism. I realised that the force of tradition still held a tight grip on the hearts and minds of my three associates.

The approaching identification-card deadline was having the effect Satchoo had predicted. People did come in to have their photos taken, but nowhere near as many as was required to cover the costs, that is, to cover the costs of the R40 a month rent, the R40 a month wages and the daily expense of films, chemicals, printing paper, water and electricity. Within three weeks there were definite signs that the studio wasn't going to be a success and by the sixth week it was obvious that it would have to be written off. My first month's salary was outstanding. But I had received almost half of it by using (with Satchoo's approval) some of the cash takings for my personal expenses that couldn't wait till the end of the month.

Satchoo worked and lived in Jo'burg. He came down to Pretoria every weekend to inspect his business. Gona lived in Pretoria but worked in Jo'burg; his share of the partnership was severely and unfairly demanding; for after a long day's work (which included travel to and from Johannesburg) he'd call in the evenings to help in the darkroom.

Satchoo now began to stay away from the studio altogether. Gona and I decided that it was best to pull out also. Natoo, who hitherto had been a sort of sleeping partner, now decided that he would run the studio himself until he had recovered his capital. It was, of course, a desperate, penny-wise-pound-foolish endeavour. But I reluctantly agreed to help him for two weeks.

In the meanwhile Gona, who worked for Klotz, a Johannesburg photographic wholesaler, obtained an interview for me with a Greek photographer in Bree Street. I went there but the Greek received me in a surly manner and, without ceremony, put me to work in the darkroom. I did what I could but developing photos of whites made me a little nervous; so my first efforts weren't exactly perfect. My Greek boss looked at the results and said my work wasn't good enough and that I didn't have enough experience. He agreed to take me on as an apprentice; he would provide my travel expenses and my lunch but there would be no wages.

When I left the studio that evening, I gave the Greek owner no definite response and he didn't solicit any. Throughout the day I spent there I had the impression that he either took an instant dislike to me or that he was naturally churlish or, perhaps, he was just pretending to be churlish. Anyway, I had the impression that, no matter what the quality of my work, he was only interested in engaging me as an apprentice.

I dismissed the studio experience, like a traveller who doubles back after having taken the wrong turning. I scoured the advertisement columns of the *Pretoria News*, the *Star*, and the *Rand Daily Mail*. I told myself: "Ag, it won't be difficult. I always, in the end, obtain what I'm after." Yet, the newspapers didn't turn out what I was on the lookout for. The finds, when they did appear, were meagre and unflattering. After several weeks of careful searching I found a vacancy for a young, intelligent, "Coloured" or Indian male somewhere in the centre of Johannesburg. Since I made the discovery in the evening, I decided to take the train the next morning, the train after the one that the students normally took. I put on my best suit, after having a clean shave, and felt confident that I looked like a new sixpence.

After some searching, I located the place. I found a greasy shack-like building. One of the "Coloured" workers there (he was young and dressed in a pair of heavily stained overalls) led me to a white woman seated behind a desk in a tiny office. The woman was surprisingly courteous. She carefully explained what I was required to do. The job seemed simple enough. I kept my eyes open and understood that the place specialized in selling and rehauling car batteries. The work they demanded was one of simple maintenance: the batteries that were packed on shelves had to be removed and filled regularly with distilled water.

"Oh yes," I said, "I can do the work!" I tried to express enthusiasm but, deep down, pangs of doubt and disappointment set in. Hurt spread like an internal haemorrhage at the thought that I was desperate enough to think of accepting such a menial job. But I swallowed my pride.

"I can start immediately," I emphasized. The white woman, looking at once regretful and confused, said she would let me know sometime next week. A week passed and no reply came. I decided I'd return to the place to find out what happened. When I got there, one of the "Coloured" chaps, who was busy handling some batteries, told me that the woman who had interviewed me was out. When he saw that I was willing to wait, he told me straight out that it was no use waiting as the job was already gone: "Given to an Indian chap with a standard six pass. Look the laanie told me you were better qualified to do some sort of desk job, not a manual job like this. So man, there's no point you're wasting your time here!"

* * *

It's so strange the way the world behaves towards you when you're not working. It was warm clear blue-skied days but I moved and struggled through a thick mist of disapproval. Faces stared, maybe I imagined them; silent words goaded me, perhaps they were words of my own mind. Everywhere I saw unmoving lips and hard unsmiling eyes reproaching, reprimanding, reproofing: Why aren't you working? Why don't you find a job?

The innocent world of boyhood, the easy teenage years, all of a sudden seemed so far away. Without a job, my matric certificate was nothing; without a regular income, I was nothing, *niks* and bugger-all.

Raymond Ernest failed his English exam again and so wasn't able to obtain his matric. What was more natural than that the two failures should spend a lot of time together. But neither he nor I had any money. Sometimes we used to scrape together enough to make up our bio fare. I saw two films with Raymond: Hemingway's *Adventures of a Young*

Man and *Fanny*. Both made him even more determined to go overseas.

Thanks to Raymond I discovered the Cape part of the Location, that is, that part of the Location between Blood and Struben Streets where the "Coloureds" lived. Raymond himself lived in Struben Street with his sister and married brother.

One day he borrowed his brother's Vespa scooter and invited me to go with him to Laudium. The Location had been declared a white zone in the Fifties and ever since there had been vague talk that all the inhabitants would one day have to leave and go eight miles away to a place called Claudius. Later, when houses started appearing, the township was renamed Laudium.

We got on to Von Wielligh Street, passed into Church Street, passed the great towering chimneys of Iscor and negotiated a winding road towards Attridgeville (the African location) and, finally, as the road swung and rose, we came upon a huge sprawling clearing. On the left, just before we turned off on the right to leave the road stretching towards the Kyalami race track, I noticed there was a white policeman standing on a knoll, rifle in hand, keeping watch. In the field (about a hundred yards away) a group of African workers in red cotton shirts and shorts were toiling away. The words of Sam Cooke's 'Chain Gang' invaded my mind:

All day long they work so hard
Working their lives away.

Raymond Ernest, his eyes fixed on the road, interrupted with a shout: "Hey Jay, if you want to see a prison farm, look on your left!"

When we entered Laudium, the place reminded me of Lenz: a residential quarter still in a period of gestation. We found the house of Nathan's parents.

Nathan was a distant cousin. He and his family used to live in the backyard of a Cowie-Street block near Barber Street. I recalled they had an uncomfortable two-roomed place and the usual communal toilet and "bathroom." Nathan's mother, a half-cousin of my father, made us welcome and provided us with tea and some Tennis biscuits. Nathan was in and he showed us around. The brick house was small, modern and comfortable. What surprised me was the space around the house: there was a huge clearing for a garden in front and a larger one for a yard at the back. Definitely better than the Location, I thought. But I didn't say anything; I recalled an Indian Congress leaflet calling on the people to resist the move to Laudium.

Nathan took us on a guided tour and, as he identified the various houses, I realized that the people who had moved were either the poor or the badly housed. At one moment Nathan pointed to a house and said, "This is where Tilak lives — you know the guy who used to play for Delfos?"

"Yes", I nodded.

As we rode back I forgot the sun, the glinting light and the rush of warm air: my thoughts turned to Tilak. Three or four years ago he played football, dressed well and, when you met him at the Corner, he had time to stand and talk. He had a fine physique, was a good footballer with a good dribble and a good shot; when he was well dressed, he looked neat and elegant; he had good taste and he was always wearing something new and different. Now, he no longer played football and was rapidly developing a paunch, his hair was losing its lustre, his dressing had become plain and predictable, and, when you now met him, he was content to say, "Hello and see you."

I was sure it was married life, family life that did that. His whole existence seemed to be devoted to earning a living and making ends meet. I recalled his wife, Durga. Boy! how attractive she used to be in her courting days. Now she was a mother and had the excess fat to prove it. A year ago, I remember, I paid Tilak a visit. Thank God, he is still the decent nice guy of old. We started off talking about films, football, clothes and soon, without us realizing it, we were talking about the cost of living, the price of bread and the lousy wages he received. I went away thinking: after marriage the only other big event left in life is death.

I felt depressed. What a fall, what a mess. In my mind's eye, I saw his kids, his wife, his house. From now on until

194

his last days this was it. Prices, rent, kids, job, wife and Laudium. Was this the great promise of growing up and becoming a man?

A traffic light stopped us somewhere in Church Street. Raymond recognized someone in a van on the opposite side of the road. He waved; I did not recognise anybody. Later I spotted a Greek fish and chips shop and immediately felt hungry but I was broke.

The rush of air, once the Vespa took off, sent me back to my thoughts: imagine getting your matric, your teacher's certificate and then settling down in this dump, this desert of boredom and pettiness, where the only excitement is a good football match, and even that, nowadays, was rare.

No, I know life must be different. It simply must be. Just to accept things, as if they were fixed and immutable, is to throw in the towel and to forfeit the challenge of life. Hell, I can't just give in like that. I must make an attempt to get one look at the outside world. In Hemingway's *Adventures of a Young Man* Richard Beymer in the film at least tried to do something. No, if I stay here, I'll end up like Tilak, like a bird caught in birdlime. A job, a job. I gotta get a job.

* * *

Perry, a Durbanite, who used to work for my father on the market phoned me one morning. He had left the Market, got married and was now living in Germiston.

Indian Natalians weren't allowed either to work or to stay in the Transvaal, but Perry was so full of nerve and opportunism that he managed against all the odds, and by hook and (I suspect, mainly) by crook, to work and stay, that is, by always being just one jump ahead of the white authorities.

He was thin and handsome, and his movements were swift and sharp, which made him look like a waiter having to attend too many tables. He had a neat head, a dainty moustache, a set of slightly rabbity teeth and like so many Durban Tamils an authentic Dravidian colour. He had, besides, a good Tamil singing voice and an unsurpassed talent for lying.

I see him on a certain Saturday morning accosting an

195

Afrikaans customer. His Afrikaans was recently acquired and limited — the Natalians didn't learn Afrikaans at school — but he managed a hail-fellow-well-met, *goeie môre meneer*! And he produced the inevitable smile on the unsuspecting Afrikaner's face and made him return the greeting with clumsily concealed conceit and smug condescension: *môre jong!*

Depending on the reply, he measured whether he could push or limit his advantage. A severe reply met with silence; a quick enthusiastic reply met with the same over-loud voice laced with hidden laughter: *Hoe gaan dit meneer*? The reply was nearly always cheery and trusting. It wasn't Perry's intention to clinch a sale, at least not his first intention, but I saw it happen over and over again, as it happened then, the white man, happy and flattered with the royal respect accorded him, found himself, willy-nilly, obliged to buy a box of tomatoes or a bag of potatoes. This reaction of the white man always caused Perry to titter. I see him composing himself, going over to my cousin Bala and boasting how he had just made a sale. Perry (his real name was Perumal), in one way or the other, always livened up Saturdays.

"Hey, how's it man?" Everything Perry said, even the most innocent remark, always sounded facetious.

"OK — still, unemployed, though!"

"Hey man, that's why I'm phoning. Here's a lekker job here — here, where I'm working. You know, I'm working for Milk Maid Ice Cream. They want a sort of despatch clerk and general office worker. I'm sure you can do the job. It's a lekker desk job."

"What about pay?"

"Ten Rands a week."

"Ja, that sounds all right. Well, what do I do?"

"Are you free now?"

"Ja."

"Well, take the Jo'burg train and get off at Doornfontein. Just outside the station, you'll see Sherwell Street; the place is just there. You'll see a white Volkswagen Combi with Milk Maid on it standing outside."

I took the train and got the job.

27

I balked when we got to the Europeans only entrance of the
Johannesburg Pass Office. I looked at him (this was our first
trip together) and showed him the sign, indicating more with
expression than with words: "I can't go in there." But he
brushed this aside with a oh-I'm-not-bothering-with-that-
nonsense gesture, and I was forced, timidly, to follow. He
went straight to one of the counters, addressed a young
white man and, in correct but heavily accented English, said:
"I'm from Milk Maid Ice-Cream, this is my office clerk, will
you explain to him all about the pass business please!" The
man behind the counter was not at all pleased to see me, but
I adopted an uncomfortable I'm-with-him pose.

My boss, De Beer, was a Dutchman. He knew some English
but not enough to feel confident; so he spoke Dutch and I
(and the others) spoke to him in Afrikaans. And I thought I
had finished with Afrikaans. I didn't mind it though. Using
Afrikaans with him was different. There was no underhand
game of domination or subjugation involved. Afrikaans was
merely a medium of communication.

De Beer, tall and blond and lean, was fairly good looking.
He had a slightly loping walk and his movements suggested
impatience and drive. I learnt that he had been in the country only some eight or ten months.

The pass business was long and complicated. A tax on
every "boy" engaged by the Company had to be calculated in
a roundabout and very bureaucratic way. But I made a men-
tal note of the various explanations and I felt reasonably confident that I had understood the essentials.

The first or second Saturday after that, Ajax of Amsterdam,
who were over on a short tour, were playing at the Rand

Stadium against a Southern Transvaal eleven. Perry, who always bought the *Rand Daily Mail*, said (in Afrikaans), "Hey Boss, your fellow countrymen are playing today." And I innocently added: "Man, it sure would be nice to see that match."

I remember De Beer saying: "Look, there isn't much to do now! Jay and I will go to the Stadium." At first, I thought he was joking but about half an hour before the match started, I found myself in his grey Morris Minor, one of those small distinctly British cars, and on my way to the Stadium.

On the way there a billboard-advertisement of S. Hirschmann caught De Beer's eye: *When you see me, don't think of Insurance, but when you think of Insurance, see me.* He asked me to explain the meaning of the catch phrase. Then he requested me to help him by speaking to him exclusively in English. He confided that it was necessary for him to improve his command of the language because some of his superiors in Pretoria were Englishmen. I tried to oblige but it was no good; he relapsed, without even realizing it, into Dutch and I felt loath to call him to order.

When we reached the Stadium, I noticed he had once again forgotten that we would have to enter through separate entrances and that we wouldn't be allowed to sit together. In the event Ajax weren't all that they were cracked up to be but I didn't tell him this. He kept complaining that the South Africans were really dirty players.

I met his wife once or twice. She was rather a plain woman, *petite* and with slightly rabbity teeth. There was nothing in her physique that set her off or marked her out from other white women that I saw passing in the street outside; but the way she spoke to me, the open friendliness she displayed and the interest she showed were all markedly un-South African.

One morning I met her at the Depot; she looked visibly shaken and touched.

"Have you heard Jay?" she asked me with an unfamiliar anxiety. I didn't know what she was on about. I had no radio and had seen no paper that morning.

"Kennedy has been assassinated!"

198

The news surprised me but if home politics was already remote, overseas politics was something of the nether world. I wondered why she was making such a fuss. I would have been touched if she had said that Frank Sinatra or Elvis Presley or somebody else like that had been assassinated, but Kennedy meant almost nothing to me. I had, after all, remained pretty indifferent when, a couple of years earlier, Verwoerd was almost assassinated. When, however, I saw the *Star* that evening, I realized that perhaps I had underestimated the importance of the event.

* * *

Perry introduced me to what was to become one of my principal tasks.

"Look, all you have to do is to supply them with ice-cream and note down what was supplied. This chap, for instance, Nelson, number 36 — we give these guys numbers because there's more than one Nelson amongst them — he wants ten suckers. So you count ten suckers and you note down his name, number and the date here (he pointed to a ledger-sized, receipt book), and the amount of ice-cream: ten suckers, ten cups, twelve chocolinas, one family brick, eight wafers and so on. OK?"

It seemed fairly simple, so I nodded understandingly.

"And then you do all the other guys in the same way. We divide them into two groups. You do the guys on this side and I'll do the guys on that side."

He pointed to a long narrow counter. In front the vendors, the "boys," were milling about. Some had already put on the white overalls with the bold red lettered Milk Maid motif embroidered on the back; others had it rolled up and held against the seats of their bicycles; others again had it flung carelessly across the fibreglass ice boxes, the large and bulky ice-cream containers, which looked like gigantic pumpkins squashed into rectangles; some were queueing up for their stock and eager to start their day; others, looking more experienced, clustered about discussing, now in calm now in clamour, now in Tswana now in Afrikaans; one or two iso-

199

lated themselves in the corner of the large hall and slowly and methodically ate their breakfast bought from the café next door (usually a half loaf of white bread and tea drunk from an old jam tin); and one or two were having their bicycles attended to by John, the tall and soft-spoken bicycle "boy". The dense sound of muscular movement and voices rose, fell and rose again. The various bodies, men and bicycles, like specks of strong white clouds floated across the grey cement floor and drifted out through the double-doored exit.

"When they're gone out, we stop for a coffee break. No colour bar here, you know! The boss's wife makes coffee for us, and she even serves us. And the cups aren't kept separate! She doesn't come so often now but she's really a nice friendly woman.

"After coffee we sit down and do our totals."

He lifted his head and, with a quick nod, said, "Over there!" I followed his indication and saw a low brick wall cut off a corner of the hall and, like a fence, demarcate the makeshift administrative section of the Depot. Two wooden desks, a metal cabinet, a huge wall calendar and a black telephone broke the stark atmosphere of the office. One of the two desks faced the door. This was my desk. The other was De Beer's. Perry didn't have a desk; he went out with the Volkswagen Combi delivering ice-cream to cafes, bringing in bicycles that had broken down or re-supplying those "boys" who, having had a windfall sale, wanted more ice-cream but were too far out to make their way back to the Depot.

"You have ten suckers at four cents; so you have forty cents; ten wafers, ten cups etc., etc. Then you add up everything and you get a total. Most of these guys don't take more than three or five Rands worth of stuff. William 95 and Zacharia 86 — they're the clevas of this place — take out at least ten Rands. Both guys got a school. They're dangerous bastards. Have you seen? They both carry kierries. Zacharia buggered up a 'boy' from Wall's Ice-Cream one day — the guy had the nerve: he wanted to sell his ice-creams at Zacharia's school."

I couldn't as yet fix any faces to any of the names, except

200

for the bicycle "boy" John, and the coffee and stockroom "boy" Hendrik.

"Then, we've got practically nothing to do until five o'clock. After that the 'boys' start coming in. Then you must take back what they haven't sold. Check to see if they're not smelted — spoilt — and then you total up, and then you subtract the total from this morning's total and that's the amount they must pay you.

"Some of these guys will give you the exact amount. But most of them will empty their pockets and put all the coins on the counter. You must sort them out — you know, put all the cents, the five cents, the ten cents and so on together — and then count everything, in front of them. Most of the time they're a little short; so you must note this, tell them, explain to them, ask them why they're short. This is important, heh, you know."

It didn't take me long to get used to the routine. Reddy, an amiable Tamil from Germiston, was the third and final member of the administrative staff. He was older than us and was a family man. He actually ran a depot in nearby Roodepoort but he brought the cash of each day's takings to the Doornfontein Depot; so Reddy was around during the mornings and evenings and, sometimes, during lunch time. He drove a small Ford lorry with the usual Milk Maid markings.

One afternoon the *Star* featured a front-page article on Dennis Brutus, the "Coloured" poet and Chairman of the South African Non-racial Olympic Committee. It reported he had been shot, wounded and arrested by the police in a nearby Johannesburg street. This incident troubled me, at least more than the death of Kennedy did.

Some weeks later, during the routine coffee break, I cornered Perry in the presence of Reddy and said, "Hey, remember how you once said that here there are no separate cups and saucers. How is it that now I see the boss always using the same cup and saucer; and how is it that Hendrik now makes sure not to mix his things with ours?"

He looked a little embarrassed but said defensively: "I wasn't pulling a fast one, ask Reddy."

201

Reddy clicked his tongue: "Tschit, nah man, you know Jay, De Beer's wife used to make coffee for us, and she used to serve us."

"Yes," I interrupted, "Perry has already told me about that."

"Nah, you know, he goes to Pretoria, and you know, how they are there."

* * *

Milk Maid was a subsidiary of Pretoria Diaries. De Beer went to Pretoria to report on the progress of the Depot. Sometimes he stayed over for the weekend. It was possible that he was being coached to be properly South African in his behaviour towards "non-whites". I remember whenever his two white seniors came up fròm Pretoria — one of them, like him, was a Hollander, the other was an Englishman — they treated us with stiff formality and their attitude was generally cold and condescending. But still I thought Perry and Reddy's estimation of De Beer's non-segregation was optimistic. I noticed already on the second day that John (the bicycle repairer) and Hendrik (the coffee maker), and all the other "boys", used one set of toilets; Reddy, Perry and I used another; while De Beer, exclusively, used a third. This last toilet was in the stockroom and was kept under lock and key. De Beer of course had a key and Hendrik, because he was responsible for the upkeep of the toilet and also because he was in charge of the sugar, the coffee, the tinned milk, the receipt books, the overalls and the bicycle spares had another.

When I came in one morning, I was surprised to see Hendrik with a fresh black eye and a huge swelling around the mouth. He must have got into a fight, I concluded. The area around the Depot was, after all, just outside the station, and I remember one evening when I was on my way to get a train — the station was about two hundred yards from the Depot — I saw an African lying in the gutter: he had been stabbed and was bleeding profusely. Two white policemen were standing over him and one of them said: "Hey Kaffir, moenie hier sterwe nie!" There was also, not that long ago, the killing next door of the Indian café owner and his wife during a petty hold-up. Yes, I was sure, Hendrik must have been waylaid by one or other of the thugs who hung around the place.

But later when De Beer came in, he looked smirkishly jovial. He turned towards me and said, proudly: "Did you see how smart Hendrik looks today?" The evident bravado and the lack of compassion of the remark surprised me. I was expecting him to show more concern for his favourite "boy".

"Yes. What happened?"

"Didn't he say anything?"

"No, I don't think it's easy for him to speak with his mouth in that condition."

"I fixed him up like that!"

"What!"

"Yes, I came in early this morning and when I got here, I saw this blighter — he was using my toilet, behind my back. Can you beat that? So I let him have it then and there. That'll teach him!"

* * *

Gona arranged for me to board and lodge with his aunt, who lived just a block away in Rocky Street. I knew the Naidoos (who didn't?). They were a celebrated political family. The father had been, it was said, a protegé of Gandhi and I had known Murthi, one of the three sons, at Tamil School, and had had a nodding acquaintance with Indres, the eldest son, who was serving a long-term sentence for sabotage on Robben Island; and I knew Shantie, the eldest girl, who was constantly being harassed by the Special Branch. It made a change being with them. I didn't have a room of my own, meals were exclusively vegetarian, and very modest, and there was no hot running water; but I was made welcome and it was convenient being so close to work.

It was during the second week of my stay with them that the family, except for the mother, decided to go to the Majestic cinema in Fordsburg to watch *Lawrence of Arabia*. Murthi invited me to come along and I readily accepted. Just

203

before we left the house on that warm evening, however, two of Shantie's friends joined us. Shantie's friends, curiously, were young white girls — they were probably acquainted through political commitment. I also had the impression they might have been first or second year university students. Once again the idea of being in the company of whites all at once intimidated and fascinated me. I had hoped there would be a chance to approach them and talk to them, although I didn't think I'd know what to say, save to declare that I aimed to leave the country, but the entire evening was severely segregated. Shantie and her younger sister, Assoo, and the two white girls remained in front while Murthi, Perumal (his younger brother) and I remained at the back, and when we were seated in the cinema the girls were all on one side and we boys were all on the other.

Inside the cinema, however, the only thing that mattered was Peter O'Toole and Omar Sharif. Their performances impressed while the eerie desert scenes and the exciting colours thrilled me; but I sensed that I didn't quite understand the film. I came out of the cinema feeling uneasy and a little disappointed. Yet I was certain that the white girls would say something that would make it less obscure and give to it the intelligence and comprehension that I was incapable of giving it.

I had always wondered about the superiority of the whites, not only above us Indians but also above everybody else who wasn't white. How was it that their domination was so naked and evident? How was it that they were so superior in every field? How was it that they were with their Samson, Hercules, Tarzan and Superman stronger? How was it that they were with their Galileo, Harvey, Pasteur and Einstein cleverer? How was it that they were with their Jesus, St. Francis of Assisi and Albert Schweitzer more moral? How was it that they were with their Leonardo da Vinci, Michelangelo, Van Gogh and Toulouse Lautrec more artistic? How was it that they were with their Denis Compton, Rocky Marciano and Stanley Matthews sportingly superior? How was it that they were and are with their Hedy Lamarr and Rock Hudson, Elizabeth Taylor and Tony Curtis, and Grace

Kelly and Gary Grant more beautiful. I looked in the mirror and asked, "Mirror, Mirror on the wall who is the fairest, the wisest and the ablest of them all?" And back came the answer: "The whites in South Africa, the whites in America, the whites in Europe".

I kept my ears open in anticipation of a wise white reply. Eventually one of them interrupted the silence of the night air: "Oh, wasn't the colour magnificent?" while the other added: "Oh, I simply loved the desert!"

* * *

A few days later,I bought and read Harper Lee's *To Kill a Mocking Bird*. After reading it, I couldn't help putting down my thoughts on paper. It was evolution, I wrote, that gave us different skin colours. The sun made the skin of those who lived nearer to it darker than those who lived farther away. Logically the whites would one day themselves, through the long process of evolution, be black.

I was also at that time reading *The Merchant of Venice*. Raymond had asked me to help him pass his English exam, which, of course, meant would I write the exam for him. I hesitated, wondered if the fraud could be carried out without risk but the challenge, of the exam and not the fraud, attracted me; so I accepted. Most of the set books I had studied for matric were still on the English syllabus; the only change was the replacement of *Julius Caesar* by *The Merchant of Venice*. Anyway, I came across the words of Shylock; he isn't the best character in the play but this particular reflection of his touched me:

Hath not a Jew eyes? Hath not a Jew hands, organs,
dimensions, senses, affections, passions, fed with the
same food, hurt with the same weapons, subject to
the same diseases, healed by the same means, warmed
and cooled by the same winter and summer, as a Christian
is? If you prick us, do we not bleed? If you tickle us,
do we not laugh? If you poison us, do we not die? And if
you wrong us, shall we not revenge?

I copied it down on the same piece of paper where I had made my note about evolution and racialism. When I had finished, I slipped the paper into the drawer alongside other bits of papers, a stapler, a ruler, pens, pencils, a rubber and some rubber bands and practically forgot about it. Until one day, when I wasn't in the office, De Beer came across it.

I worked from Sunday to Sunday and every two weeks I had a Sunday and a Monday off. These two days were most welcome, not only because I could rest but also because I could go back to the familiarity, the comfort and the security of 226; and it was during one of these breaks that De Beer found the paper. At first, in a teasing manner, he praised me, but then — it was really curious — my jottings led him to a defence of apartheid.

He conceded that someone like myself ought to have the same rights as a European but such rights, he stressed, couldn't be granted to all the Indians, and certainly not to the Africans. "The Africans are ignorant. They are dirty. And they stink. And you know," he lowered his voice, "even Reddy's place has an unpleasant odour about it."

Reddy of course was a modest chap but he had dignity and was personally as clean as any one of us. I knew from football visits that the Germiston Location was a cesspool of a place. It wasn't Reddy but the environment that was in question. But I didn't defend Reddy. "Well, why don't you come to my place you'll see that all the Indians don't live the same way."

"Yes, but it's not just the living; you see it's everything. Take the food, for instance, Indian food stinks!"

This reproach bowled me over. I could barely react. All I did was to betray dismay but my speechlessness wasn't spared; for while I was still reeling under the impact of the reproach he said, "Anyway, South Africa is a white country not a black country. The whites got here before the blacks."

It was the first time I had heard such a claim. In a vague way, I thought just as the Indians under Gandhi and Nehru obtained their independence and the Ghanians theirs, the Africans in South Africa would one long and distant day have their independence; but the idea that South Africa

206

wasn't black was to my ears like saying springboks didn't spring and bees didn't sting. Yet not being used to debates of this sort — even in College my intellectual contests were more ruminated than spoken — I stood there flummoxed and flabbergasted. All I could do, and that too with little assurance, was to say: "I don't know all the answers. I'm not interested in politics, you know. But I'll ask someone who is better informed and then we can continue this discussion."

De Beer was visibly pleased with his performance. I felt unsettled. It was as if I had a footballer in front of me that I, for some inexplicable reason, could neither dribble nor tackle.

That night I told the Naidoos about the discussion I had had with De Beer. They said, "The Dutchman is talking nonsense" and felt satisfied that they had with that settled the matter. I wasn't convinced, but I was afraid to say so lest I force them into the uncomfortable position that I myself had experienced earlier. It was strange but after such a long time I suddenly missed Jopa.

The days, weeks and months passed quietly until it was time to sit for Raymond Ernest's exam. I obtained permission to take off three days. I had done my reading and felt confident I could do what was necessary. What nagged me though was the strategy. How exactly was the deception going to be performed?

When we reached the venue, somewhere in Proes Street, I was quite surprised to see so many students. I was also surprised to see that a majority of them were older than Raymond and myself. Each student was issued with an official number. An invigilator, a white woman, came round to check the slips of papers that contained the printed name and number of each exam candidate. After the invigilator had completed her checking, Raymond filled in my number in the boxed space that was provided on the top of each of the double-sheeted foolscap papers, and I filled in Raymond's number on mine. We were both mindful that the numbers we had filled in would never be exposed, thus denying the invigilator the temptation to verify them against those on our respective candidate slips.

The ploy was no more complicated than that. Raymond, as

anticipated, passed comfortably; I, as was expected, failed
lamentably.

Two weeks later I learnt, from Sattar, that Raymond had
left the country and that he had joined Bhiraj and Innie in
London.

28

Living so near to the Depot turned out to be more bother than convenience. Stock deliveries from Pretoria were sometimes made in the middle of the night. So because I was nearby, De Beer simply instructed me, as if it was a part of my ordinary duties, to be on hand at ten o'clock to check the delivery. After two such deliveries I thought the best solution would be to get away; besides, living with the Naidoos had its drawbacks: I was far away from Fordsburg, where all the cinemas and cafes were located, and I missed the comfort of hot running water.

I had made it known to some of the people at the College that I was looking for a room in Fordsburg. Boykie, the chap who had been on the Grahamstown-Cape Town trip with me, phoned one afternoon and informed me that his mother owned a little place that had a room I could use.

My new home was in a small ill-lit side street. The room was tiny; adjoining it was a large bare bathroom, which contained a bathtub and a single, cold water tap. The whole makeshift nature of the place was characterized by the lockless front door. But all I wanted was somewhere to sleep.

Fortunately for me my sister Ruby, who had married some years before, was then living in Fietas. So I took the train at Doornfontein and, one station farther down the track, got off at Braamfontein, walked down a long badly lit tunnel — the same one I used when I went to College except that I now went in the opposite direction — got out on to Seventh Street and from there made the long lonely walk in the night towards my sister's place.

She by then had a baby boy. Her husband, a Pretoria fellow, worked for a Memon outfitters' shop in Market Street. Her barely convenient home had a rudimentary outdoor bath-room, which provided, if a fire was made in the kitchen stove, a hot shower. Ruby took care of my washing. So in some ways I was still pampered like I had been in Jerusalem Street. But I didn't go to her place every evening. Sometimes I got out of the tunnel at the Fordsburg end, picked up a sandwich at one of the cafes (as if he was a College student again) and then went to one of the cinemas, or otherwise I simply went to sleep early.

Now when I think of it, there were many nights when I longed for the presence of Soobathie. Thoughts of her warmth, her smile, her sensuous body ate into my loneliness. How many times I went to bed feeling alone and abandoned. Nobody knew me in Fordsburg and nobody seemed to care. I sensed, though only fleetingly, that in leaving the Location I had left something of myself behind. Sometimes I comforted myself by singing Frank Sinatra's 'All alone'.

* * *

One quiet Friday afternoon De Beer and I were in the office. I was busy making up the wage packets when the phone rang. De Beer picked up the phone, looked at me with a sporting grin on his face and then, with the eye movements of complicity, indicated that it was for me. I was greeted by a beautiful female voice, which teasingly defied: "Guess who's speaking?" It was embarrassing. I had no idea who it was.

"It's Prali. You know, I'm at the College."

I connected the voice to the face.

"How did you know I was here?"

"Oh, I knew from some of the Pretoria people at the College and — wait a minute there's someone who wants to say hello to you."

"Hey Jay, how's it?"

I instantly recognised the voice of Sattar. I knew he was at Wits doing a B.Sc. degree and was, like the College students, a commuter. We still met whenever I returned to the Location and we were still very close friends.

"Hey Sattar, what's up? What's happening?"

Sattar spoke at his excited, machine-gun pace: "No man, it was too tiring travelling every day; so I decided I'd find somewhere to stay in Fordsburg. I'm living at Prali's place. I've got a room. Do you know where they live?"

"No. No idea at all!"

"Well, they live in Terrace Road. It's not very far from your place. Come and visit us tonight."

"Terrace Road?"

"Ja."

"What number?"

"Twenty-four."

"OK, I'll see you tonight."

At College I had tended, because Prali was Dravidian in colour, not to look at her as carefully or as closely as I could have. That night, under the multiple ceiling light of the front room, I saw a finely chiselled face with a Grace Kelly nose and a beautiful set of pearly white teeth; and I heard a sophisticated and melodious voice. I noticed she was tall and that she carried and controlled her body, though she was slightly bow-legged, with elegance and mannequin-like poise. But even more remarkable was her transparency: there was nothing phoney about her.

That night I was happy to meet Sattar and to visit the Pather house. Prali's mother, a widow, was unobtrusively charming; her two brothers and a sister were very open and friendly. From that night on, 24 Terrace Road became a substitute for 226.

Had I not resolved to leave the country, Prali, I'm sure, would eventually have become my girlfriend. She phoned me regularly at work, sent her uncle, who was a principal of a school somewhere on the Reef, with Sunday lunch; introduced me to mushroom curry and looked after me when I was laid out with flu.

* * *

The autumn days passed by and I was slowly finding my niche in the workplace. But, even then I sensed my ignorance of the laws of the country. It wasn't as if I was totally

211

unaware of the pass and the specials. I'd seen my uncles on the market sign passes and sometimes provide specials, but I had no practical sense of what they implied and even at the Depot it took me a little while to grasp their implications. De Beer used to sign all the passes and to issue all the specials himself, but with time and with his general policy of making me responsible for more and more — he even allowed me to take the keys of both the Depot and the safe home — he now authorised me to sign the passes and to hand out the specials.

It was then that I recognized the exceptional power they gave. I saw the way the "boys" queued up to have their passes signed and I realized that if I didn't sign their book (why was the Pass called a reference book?) they'd all be liable for arrest. This implication, too, I didn't grasp immediately. At first I signed the passes thinking it was a mere formality but I noticed there were one or two "boys" who no longer worked at the Depot, and who yet, towards the end of the month, came to me and asked me, very deferentially, to sign their passes. And when I complied I was surprised to see how grateful and appreciative they were. It puzzled me but I put it down to their natural civility. Then De Beer asked me one day if I was signing the passes of "boys" who no longer worked for the Depot. I replied ambiguously, saying that it was possible I might have done so but only inadvertently.

"Well, in future don't sign their passes. They're real skelems."

I ignored the injunction.

I hadn't realized that there was a curfew law exclusively applicable to Africans. I discovered that if a "boy" wanted to go out to the cinema, or elsewhere in the evening, he had to have a special, that is, a slip of paper with the following words: I the employer of Milk Maid Ice-cream hereby authorize Henry Nkosi (or whoever) to be out tonight, Wednesday, 21/1/64 (or whenever) between eight o'clock and midnight; and bearing the dated signature of the employer. There were roneo copied slips where I just had to fill in the missing details and sign. But sometimes the Depot ran out of these and I then had to write out the entire note. Almost every evening about five or more "boys" requested me to give them a special. If I refused, it meant that they couldn't go out that night, or that they could go out at the risk of being arrested.

Henry 23 was one of nature's slow coaches. He was always the last to go out and the last to come in. Yet he was a likeable fellow, funny and always cheerful but never, never punctual. It didn't worry me when he went out late in the mornings, at least not too much, although it delayed my coffee break and retarded the work of totalling up, but in the evenings when all the "boys" were in, the metal cash boxes were in the safe and I was all set to finish my day and go, waiting for Henry 23 was a real annoyance. On one particular evening he came in at least forty minutes late. I complained and mildly rebuked him for not showing more consideration. Henry 23 made no excuses but hung his head in shame. I checked him in. Henry 23 had netted a miserable sale and he was, on top of it, short.

Anyway, I had put the last sum of cash into the safe, checked to see if everything was in order and readied myself to lock up, when Henry 23 came up to me and requested a special. That was the last straw. I told him, not in so many words but effectively, to go to hell. What's more, I stingingly rebuked him for not having requested a special earlier when I was checking him in or, in the morning, when I was checking him out. Henry 23's only response was to look at me with his big eyes, sad and appealing, but I was so mad that I just ignored him, charged out of the Depot and ran off to the station. When I got off at Braamfontein, I suddenly realized what I had done, but by then it was too late.

* * *

When it was hot, the "boys" went out eagerly; when it was cold, they went out reluctantly and, what is more, they departed with little and they returned with much. But the advantage of a cold day was that ice-creams kept; they had no worries about "smeltings," which was their way of describing ice-creams that went off because of inadequate

213

freezing. These damaged ice-creams were the "boys" liability; so consequently "smeltings" meant a reduction in their weekly wage packet.

Of course, they complained and they demanded steam ice (dry ice). But steam ice was made available only on exceptional occasions, and then only for the handful of top "boys". The firm had devised metal slabs that contained a quick freezing liquid. These slabs, stacked in wooden racks in the room-like fridge that housed the ice-creams, worked and were serviceable when they were properly frozen. But the giant fridge was capricious: it performed well with ice-creams but imperfectly with the slabs.

On many occasions it took the "boys" some time to decide which one would best serve their purpose. They'd lick a finger and place it immediately on the slab. If the finger stuck to the metal cover instantaneously, the slab was perfect; if the sticking occurred after a fraction of a second — after a delay — the slab, though not perfect, was serviceable; and if the finger didn't stick, after a few seconds, the slab was useless. Generally, however, there were endless grumblings about the slabs, and always the complaint that they had to bear the burden of the Depot's inadequate equipment. They knew the efficiency of steam ice and had seen the top "boys" in the Depot receive steam ice. So why, they often queried, could they not have steam ice too — and why could they not have it everyday; for then there would be no "smeltings" and no losses to sustain.

On one occasion it had just rained, and the gutters were flooded and the sky remained dark and threatening. The "boys," knowing from experience that such weather had an adverse effect on the slabs, decided, quite spontaneously, not to venture out that day. Several — mostly the worst vendors — thought it would be worth while going out even with the threat of rain; for the field would be wide open and they would make a hefty sale. But the tough "boys" of the Depot, the *clevas*, dissuaded the potential mavericks with a sharp look and some blunt words — no one consequently went out that day.

I didn't understand that this was a sort of strike until two

214

white policemen — it was a mystery to me how they came to know about it — called at the Depot. They approached Perry but he sent them on to me. Was I in charge they enquired. Yes, I was in charge when De Beer, I explained, wasn't in. So they told me — it's remarkable how if you're representing a white man, they seem to forget your colour — "Ah, well we heard there's a strike on here."

"A strike? No, I don't know if it is a strike. No, they're not refusing to work because of wages or anything like that." I thought of the British film with Richard Attenborough, *The Angry Silence*. "No, it's just that the weather isn't very good and you know they're ice-cream vendors — they think their ice-creams will get spoilt if they go out. There's a chance that some might go out this afternoon, if the sun comes out."

A little later De Beer turned up. He did his damndest to get the "boys" out but they wouldn't budge. They stuck to their position that the cloudy heavy weather had an adverse effect on the slab, and that that meant "smeltings."

That afternoon as Perry and I sat in the office doing some routine administrative work, De Beer informed me that he was going to Natal and was going to recruit Zulus for the Depot. "The chaps here have become too smart. I feel like getting rid of the whole damn lot of them."

Two weeks later two large open trucks came up from Pretoria. De Beer and Perry drove off to Natal and came back with two loads of Zulus. It was effectively as if they had gone there to obtain goods.

It was both pathetic and amusing to see the fresh countrymen get off the back of the truck. They were transparently amazed by the hustle and bustle of the Johannesburg streets; and it was sad and amusing to see the experienced city boys look at them, laugh at their awkwardness, deride their glaring disorientation and poke fun at their ignorance. The "boys" at the Depot, in the main, spoke Tswana but Hendrik, now back in favour with De Beer, and John managed somehow to communicate with the new arrivals. Or that at least was the impression created amongst those who understood neither Tswana nor Zulu. De Beer addressed the Zulu in a kind of general assembly. He stood on the long checking

215

counter and was flanked by the two Tswana translators. He spent a lot of time explaining about the slab and stressing how it was necessary to always keep the ice box firmly closed, and how to avoid "smeltings." He also made the usual injunctions to work hard and not to be short, and he laid the expected emphasis on the harsh fact that all money unaccounted for would automatically be deducted from wages.

The first week was spent giving the Zulus appropriate names, numbers — most of them, however, had Biblical first names — finding them hostel places (they all had to go to Zulu hostels, something else I learnt for the first time), teaching them how to select a slab and ride a bicycle, showing them, or some of them, how to count in Rands and cents and introducing all of them to the prices of the different ice-creams. When they finally went out, two fellows came back, after two hours, with their ice boxes dripping ice-cream all over the place. When I saw them, I didn't care to think how the others were faring not only with the ice-creams but also with the busy streets and with the *tsotsis*. But when the first day came to an end, it was miraculous to see that most of them had actually coped with what at first seemed an impossible challenge.

* * *

Friday evening — pay day. There was something warm and comfortable about those crisp and brown envelope-like pay packets. I made them up according to wage sheets that came up from Pretoria. When I was busy with them that morning, I realized that the experienced "boys" were going to receive anything from two to ten or twelve Rands and that the Zulus were in for a rude shock.

Not all of them had been brought to Johannesburg by truck; some had come by train. Whether they travelled by train or truck, the food (usually a half a loaf of white bread and a mineral drink) was provided by the Depot but actually paid for by the Zulus themselves. It was, in fact, an advance on their wages. This had been explained to them but apparently neither with sufficient emphasis nor with sufficient clarity. In any case, I thought it was unfair that they should have been made responsible for this expense. As it transpired, having to account for the cost of their travel and boarding, and "smeltings," most of them received empty pay packets. And, to make matters worse, some were (according to the calculations) even indebted to the Depot, sometimes for as much as two rands. It wasn't surprising that they were outraged.

I was thankful that I wasn't given the unpleasant task of handing out those dismal packets. Wilson 2, an elderly man, had a fair hand, read and wrote English fluently, and was pretty good with figures. John and Hendrik told me that he was an ex-school teacher. I accepted this without query. I had noticed the old man's aloof and dignified bearing and had felt uncomfortable to see him go out with the others. De Beer, fortunately, had discovered his talents and had made him part of the administrative staff. De Beer wanted my duties to be limited to the office and to general supervision; so he had Wilson replace me at the checking counter. Perry and Wilson, thus, gave out the pay packets.

Even so, all the complainants were sent to me, and they came with wrought faces and bubbling words. I explained how the calculations had been made. De Beer was on hand. From time to time he chipped in with a word or two to reinforce my authority.

Pretty soon a band of six, obviously the leaders of the group, called the others together and addressed them. John and Hendrik reported that the Zulus were thinking of going back, and that many were complaining that they hadn't come to Jo'burg to work for nothing. I saw the consternation on De Beer's face. He manoeuvred adroitly; he isolated the ring leaders and convinced the others that everything, in a week's time, would be all right. "Those who are sissy enough not to be able to cope with the work can go back. This place is not for you. Tomorrow I'll give you a train ticket and you can go back to your kraals!"

Five of the leaders accepted his offer. The others decided they'd stay on, at least for a week. The next day the five turned up at the Depot. De Beer sent Hendrik to the station to obtain their one-way train tickets. Ten minutes later they had the tickets in their hands and De Beer bid them a cold farewell. The train only left late that afternoon. So throughout the morning the five sat on the pavement just outside the entrance of the Depot and with their backs against the wall, stoically soaking in the sun and the bustle of the street. At midday I went out to buy myself a parcel of fish and chips. I passed them on my way out and on my way back I couldn't help noticing how noble and yet how woebegone they looked.

As I entered the Depot, they folowed right behind me. It was obvious they wanted to speak to me, so I called Hendrik. "What's up fellows?" he enquired. They said they hadn't eaten anything since the previous night. They hadn't any money. I looked at them and recalled how De Beer had told me, just before he left that morning, "They've got their train ticket and that's all they'll get. Do you understand, Jay?"

"Yes sir," I had replied. There wasn't therefore any Depot money available for them. I explained this to them but I could see it was pointless, so I dug into my own pocket and gave them enough for each to have the standard half a loaf of bread and a cold drink, and a further half a loaf for supper. They were visibly grateful. It touched me to see the way they silently clapped their hands in small quick movements before accepting the money. But, through Hendrik, I emphasized, fearful that they might come back and solicit for more, that it was I and not the Depot that was giving them the money.

Later that day De Beer came in and he must have seen Hendrik in confidence; for he came to me and said reproachfully: "Jay, I heard you gave those Zulus money to buy food."

"Yes, I did."

"But, I distinctly told you that they were not to have anything but their train tickets."

"Yes, but I gave them my own money."

He looked at me, somewhat taken aback, and then said, with his voice suggesting that I was a model of gullibility, "Oh, you don't know how to treat these people."

218

I noted the word people because not so long ago Reddy, I remembered, opened a box of iced lollies, which he had just taken out of the fridge, and commented: "Look here Boss, these boxes should contain twenty-four suckers but they only have twenty-three. The people in Pretoria are not doing their job properly."

"What people?" De Beer shot back and, looking at Reddy with a wry smile, said, "You mean those things in Pretoria are not doing their job properly."

I wanted to tell him, "Hey man, you've hardly been here a year and you want to tell me how I should get on with these people!" but I held my tongue. Words, after all, couldn't express what I felt — so I just resigned myself to a hey-please! expression and left it at that.

* * *

Two months after the Zulus arrived the system of calculating wages was changed. There would be a sum proportional to the sale each vendor effected added to the weekly wages. One morning, to encourage the "boys", and notably the Zulus, a personal reward of twenty-five cents to the champion salesman of the day was offered.

Once the "boys" started coming in I pinned up to the wall immediately behind the check-out counter the name and number of the leading vendor, and the sale he had registered. I observed how the "boys" fixed their attention to the note, how they became involved, intrigued and excited as the name of one vendor gave way to another and as one sale amount superseded the other. There was on that day a dramatic increase in the sales.

The next day fifty cents was offered to the champion vendor. The amount of ice-cream the "boys" demanded that morning was unprecedented. Even the fellows who normally didn't take out more than four Rands took out, that day, ice-cream worth at least ten Rands. The sale amounts that evening were even better than the preceding day's. Lazarus, one of the six Zulu ring leaders, the one that stayed on, won the fifty cents prize.

219

Sometimes, on rare occasions, a "boy" didn't come in. This was always a worry, for it was impossible to know what had happened. Was he killed or injured in an accident? Was he mugged? Or did he simply decide to abandon the bicycle and make off with the proceeds? Most of the time it was these petty thefts that accounted for their absence. Someone would phone and report the sighting of a riderless Milk Maid bicycle. Perry would then go out and collect the stray property; and I would have to go to the local police station and report the alleged theft. But these calls to the police were routine; they never apprehended the missing "boy."

One evening Lazarus failed to report back. When I checked how much he had taken out, I found that he had left the Depot with more than fifteen Rands worth of ice-creams, which was an exceptional sum for one day. It was, after all, five Rands more than my own weekly wages. But ever since Lazarus had won the fifty cents prize he had been steadily going out with larger and larger stocks. I was under the impression that he must have discovered a new school or something. But now I wondered if he hadn't been planning this all along. I reported the alleged theft, knowing it was a mere formality, and appreciating that the report took me away from the Depot and provided me with an opportunity of stretching my legs.

I was quite surprised when two weeks later I was informed that Lazarus had been arrested and would be appearing in the local magistrate's court. Since I was the principal accuser, De Beer instructed me to attend the court hearing. Hendrik went with me. Once again I didn't mind being present because it made a change from the dreary routine of the Depot. We saw Lazarus. His pointed sad face graced an awkward tall body and he looked, oddly enough, calm and serene.

In court the charge was read out and I was asked to identify him. Lazarus, through a Zulu interpreter, pleaded not guilty. He defended himself by accusing me of theft. This took me completely unawares. The other checkers and I, Lazarus hotly charged, worked a fiddle with some of the vendors. I wasn't even aware that such a fiddle was possible. But now, in court, I woke up to its possibility: the checker gives

220

the "boy" twenty lollies but records only ten, the proceeds of the outstanding ten are then shared between checker and vendor on some agreed basis. God! I could have kicked myself for not having thought of that before, but how, I asked himself, could Lazarus accuse me of doing such a thing. The magistrate noted the disbelief on my face.

While the magistrate deliberated, Hendrik and I waited outside in the bare yard of the court. The African interpreter, looking like a school teacher, approached us and told me that Lazarus was a chief's son. "It's difficult for these people who come from the homelands," he said apologetically, "to understand the life here." I nodded, indicating I understood what he meant but I couldn't see what this had to do with me: I had no hard feelings towards Lazarus.

It was a warm bright sunny day. Corrugated iron sheets, painted maroon, fenced in the back of the yard. The red sand on the ground reflected the bright light and made the eye blink. Lazarus was led out. He was handcuffed but free to move within a roped off section of the yard. A white police-man desultorily surveyed the prisoners from afar. An African policeman, baton in hand, attended them more closely. Lazarus beckoned Hendrik and me. We approached and touched the rope fence. Lazarus looked at me and I was surprised to see that there was, in spite of his predicament, a sparkle in his dark weary eyes. He lifted his hand to his mouth and made the gesture of a smoker: he wanted a cigarette. But neither Hendrik nor I smoked. Then Lazarus spoke in broken Afrikaans and asked me for five cents. I gave him the money and he thanked me by silently clapping his hands.

He was sentenced to a month in jail.

On our way back to the Depot, still smarting from the unex-pected accusation in the court, I told Hendrik I couldn't under-stand Lazarus. "Why did he accuse me of being dishonest?" Hendrik looked at me and, his light-skinned face exploding in a bright, almost mocking smile, said, "Ag, jy Jay is baie goed." I accepted the compliment at its face value but as we approa-ched the Depot, it suddenly dawned on me that Hendrik must have meant that I was a bit innocent, a bit naive.

* * *

Two weeks before I left the Depot for good I met Mrs De Beer. Her visits to the place, for some reason, had become rare. De Beer must have told her that I had given in my notice and that I was leaving in two weeks. She said in an open, friendly way — she also like that French woman on the Market stood close up to me and looked me in the eye when she spoke — "So you're leaving this country?"

"Yes, I got my ticket, and I should have my passport soon — I don't think there'll be any problems."

"You're going to England?"

"Yes, to London."

"But you know, the English are phlegmatic!"

I wasn't sure what the word meant. I looked at her enquiringly, with a what-do-you-mean expression.

"You know, they're cold."

"Yes, I've heard that before but I don't think that'll bother me." I noticed her teeth were irregular and not very white. I wondered if she smoked.

"Why are you leaving?"

"Oh, it's just to get away from here. You know how it is here for non-whites."

"Well, if that's the main reason why you're leaving, why don't you go to Holland? The people there are friendlier than the English."

I smiled and said, "Well, I'm going to England first, then I'll see how things are elsewhere. I know somebody in Germany and somebody else in Holland, so there's a chance that I'll go there and maybe even settle there." She seemed pleased with this. She bid me farewell and shook my hand.

Wilson and I had become good friends. In the quiet dead moments of the afternoon we played draughts. We were pretty evenly matched. Sometimes I won, sometimes he won. I had this technique of always going for crown, even if this meant sacrificing a few of my checkers. I was convinced that the quicker you volunteered sacrifice the quicker you reaped rewards.

222

I asked him one day if he would translate a song I had heard where African words, probably Xhosa, were used. He said he would be glad to do so. John had one of those hand wound record players. I brought in an LP where Miriam Makeba and Harry Belafonte sang a number called, 'Gawuleza'. This appeal to translate the song had a reinforcing effect on our relationship. On the day I left I was surprised to learn that Wilson had organized a collection for me among the "boys"; and everybody, it seems, had made a contribution. In the end there was something like R3.25 in cash, the equivalent I was sharply aware of many a vendor's weekly wage.

29

I had my two-day week-end break a week before I left Milk Maid for good and on that Monday a police officer called at 226. I was seated in the armchair that father had occupied when policemen called at the house on the last occasion and the police officer was seated opposite on the very armchair the other policeman occupied — the one who wanted to know if I was willing to lay a charge.

"So Naidoo you want to go to England?" His English had that deep and unmistakable accent of the backveld and his gruff voice naturally matched his round face, ruddy complexion and squat figure.

"Yes, sir".

"And why do you want to go overseas?"

"Oh, just to see," I lied.

"How long will you stay?"

"A month, perhaps more".

"Will you go anywhere else?"

"Well, I'm going via France. I'm hoping I might get a chance to visit Germany, Holland and Portugal".

"Have you ever been (his voice suddenly switched tones and became solemn, intent) involved in politics at any time?"

"Oh, no. I've never been interested in politics".

"Have you been a member of the Liberal Party?"

"No".

I sensed that these last two questions, though intimidating, lacked conviction. I was certain that the Special Branch officer knew all the answers before he even thought of questioning him.

"All right Naidoo, you can go to the passport office next week and collect your passport".

Before I returned to Doornfontein, I had a long talk with my brother. This was unusual. Since our Tamil School days we had followed different paths — Ranga had his interests and I had mine. Still, my brother always came to see me play. He probably was the nearest thing I had to a fan. He like me shared my distaste for the Market. He became, like Dickie, a printer, a typographer.

"Jay, you don't know this," he said, "but Papa mortgaged the house to someone in Prinsloo Street. The Location, as you know, is going to be a white area. So this Prinsloo Street guy wants the house now while he still has time to make some rent money".

The news that 226 wasn't ours shocked me, but only momentarily. I was persuaded that nothing was permanent and besides, I was going away — what did it matter if the house was ours or not.

"When you come back from Jo'burg we'll be living in Laudium."

"Oh, you know, I'll only be staying for three weeks. I'm leaving on the eleventh of June". I showed him my Global Travels plane ticket and he finally took in the reality of my departure.

Those last three weeks in Laudium were days of wine and roses. I had nothing to do but bide my time, savour the sunny early winter days and discover Laudium. I spent much of my time walking about, taking photos of the grandiose houses that now sprang up like mushrooms in the area that somehow got baptised, Beverly Hills, and marvelled at the unbelievable contrast between the homes people occupied in the Location and the homes they now owned in Laudium. Terry Tebba, for instance, who lived with his wife in a single room, which used to be a garage, now had a sumptuous double-storeyed house fitted not only with an indoor bathroom and toilet but also with a personal toilet and bathroom fitted into his bedroom. Everyone, who in the Location had shared a yard, a single Turkish toilet and a bathless bathroom in some crowded, communal residence, now had an up-to-date home of his own with new furniture, spruce comfort and ample space. Everyone was evidently and strikingly infected with the fever to make their own homes as ostentatious, as comfortable and as modern as possible.

On the last evening before departure, I went back to the Location to have a hair-cut.

I also paid my last respects to 226.

I saw a kaleidoscope of 1950 model cars: a black Ford, a green Chevrolet, a red and white Pontiac, a cream Studebaker, a grey Oldsmobile, a red and grey Dodge, a powder blue Hudson and a maroon Plymouth — all greasy, crippled, amputated and, above all, immobile. They were spread out, choking the space in front of the houses and disseminating a general air of decay and neglect. A young Durban fellow, a motor mechanic, had settled down next to Lalie's Café and thanks to him the pavements on either side of 226 had been slowly and inevitably transformed into a motor car cemetery.

On the stoep of 226 I saw an incongruous washing line strung out with ugly dark clothes. I went up to the yard gate. It was open. I entered timidly. I saw a young woman dressed in a pair of Panjabi trousers. I addressed her: "Excuse me auntie".

"Yes," she said indifferently.

"I used to live here — you know, this used to be our house. Is it alright if I just have a quick look around?"

"Yes, it's all right". Her tired face managed a wan smile. She watched, slightly intrigued, as I walked past the kitchen doors and up to where the training room and my bedroom used to be. All the rooms, I could see, were inhabited. The place looked grimy and unkempt. It was obvious that several families now occupied the house. I didn't venture any further. I indicated with a nod of the head that I had seen enough. I thanked her, turned around and left.

GLOSSARY

arra!	*watch out! or cops!*
badja	*spiced dall-dough mixed with fresh coriander and fried in oil. Known popularly, because of its form, as 'curry balls'*
Bande Matram	*the national anthem of India*
barebies	*light dough fried in oil; also known as vetkoek*
barrie	*bumpkin or a greenhorn*
benchot	*the Gujarati equivalent of the ejaculation, 'bloody'*
Bun	*the shortened form of Banya, a Gujarati (grocer)*
caadlair	*chickpeas fried with black mustard seeds*
cajee	*an Indian deformation, perhaps, of the word, cowboy*
catty	*shortened form of catapult*
cherrie	*girl*
chore	*piss*
cleva	*smart aleck*
cowchie	*unpleasant smell of cooked meat which still betrays the odour of the animal destroyed or the smell of egg clinging to improperly washed cutlery and crockery*
crock	*jalopy*
cut up	*drunk*
Diwali	*the Hindu festival of light the nearest Hindu fete to Christmas, sometimes spelt, Deepavali*
doppeas	*peanuts*
fafi	*a chinese betting game, similar to a lottery, where each number is represented by an animal*
ganja or ganjha	*Indian hemp, dagga*

goalie	goalkeeper
halal	cosher
hommle	dribble
Jozie	Johannesburg
Kocknies	Muslim Marathis
koeksisters	doughnuts shaped like eclairs, and covered with coconut shred
kooza	cheer
kungie	penis
laat	prick, penis
lightee	kid or youngster
madressa	Muslim religious school
malalie	a slob
manjatool	turmeric
maracurry day	an all-vegetable day
marrill	a trance like condition combined with spiritual communication
mookootie	the jewel stud worn on the side of the nose
moorkoo	a Tamil savoury
mootching	stalling
naar	disgusting
pannikie	a metal bottle top
pouli sadoor	a ball or balls of sour rice
rod	a revolver, a handgun
saccra sadoor	a ball or balls of sweet rice
sambranie	a ritualized day of prayers with public offerings of food
sami	God
sammied	prayed
Satia Maa	my mother can die
skommeling	masturbating
stalling	hanging about
Tammy	familiar form for Tamil School
tannie	mother or any female elder
toppie	father or any male elder
vulca	kamatchi lamp
wittied the lingo	spoke the language
zachs	dough, money